CLOSED CIRCUIT
TELEVISION
for
POLICE

CLOSED CIRCUIT TELEVISION

for

POLICE

By

DAVID A. HANSEN

Supervising Captain
City Police Department
Daly City, California

and

JOHN J. KOLBMANN

Sergeant
Patrol Division
City Police Department
Daly City, California

With a Foreword by

Roland A. Petrocchi

Chief of Police
Daly City, California

Illustrated by

Don Campbell

CHARLES C THOMAS • PUBLISHER
Springfield • Illinois • U.S.A.

Published and Distributed Throughout the World by
CHARLES C THOMAS • PUBLISHER
BANNERSTONE HOUSE
301-327 East Lawrence Avenue, Springfield, Illinois, U.S.A.

NATCHEZ PLANTATION HOUSE
735 North Atlantic Boulevard, Fort Lauderdale, Florida, U.S.A.

© 1970 by CHARLES C THOMAS • PUBLISHER
Library of Congress Catalog Card Number: 70-135933

With THOMAS BOOKS *careful attention is given to all details of
manufacturing and design. It is the Publisher's desire to present books
that are satisfactory as to their physical qualities and artistic possibilities
and appropriate for their particular use.* THOMAS BOOKS *will be true
to those laws of quality that assure a good name and good will.*

Printed in the United States of America
PP-22

FOREWORD

S INCE becoming a policeman twenty-nine years ago, I have been privileged to witness many exciting innovations in law enforcement. In 1941 the contrast between city and suburb was sharply defined. Today city and suburb combine to form the conurbation that we witness. The problems meld with the mobility of the populations.

Solution follows problem. I have witnessed the foot patrolman replaced by the prowl car, the personal contact replaced by FM radio, the traffic motorcycle augmented by the police helicopter, and the Brownie camera replaced by television.

It has been my privilege to serve in a medium-sized department. During this era the medium-sized department has come to the fore in implementing innovative changes. In these last two decades have occurred the most far-reaching changes in the history of law enforcement.

The authors, both members of my department, are to be complimented for their documentation of the emergence of television in police work.

ROLAND A. PETROCCHI
Chief of Police

PREFACE

This book was written because we had a problem we were able to solve. During the study and research in which we engaged in order to solve our problem, we found no reference material from which to work. These writings are a compendium of our research, adaptations and results.

The problem we faced was how to maintain a continuous flow of training and other communications to the members of our rapidly growing department. Efforts to utilize tape recorders and 8mm and 16mm film achieved some success. However, the one-dimensional tape recorder was self-limiting; 8mm film proved unacceptable because of processing lags and the mechanics of editing; cost factors precluded the production of our own 16mm films; rented films also proved unacceptable. Our attention focused on the video tape technique, which has many advantages: minimal expense, portability, and instant replay.

In 1967 the Daly City Police Department set up a full-time, many-purposed, video tape recording system. Because of the newness of the media and the absence of specialized technique manuals, other law enforcement agencies have exhibited interest in the results of our program.

We are happy to pass on what we have learned. This book is written as an attempt to share our experience with other departments.

The continued encouragement and inspiration of Assistant Chief Roy J. Beecher resulted in the preparation of this manual.

CONTENTS

I

CAN YOU USE TELEVISION
IN YOUR DEPARTMENT?

Closed circuit television installation. *(Ampex Corporation)*

THE busy police administrator is forced by necessity to become a scanner. Each post brings new materials on ideas to be considered, interdepartmental correspondence piles up rapidly, police crime reports come to his attention.

Many of these matters require additional attention and study. With his severe time limitations, the efficient administrator properly delegates the necessary staff work to his subordinates.

This chapter is written with the busy administrator in mind. We present an overview of the use of television in police work for his consideration.

This writing will deal with the uses that television can serve in medium and large departments, i.e., organizations of twenty five men

3

or more. Whether a department will consider the use of television as a police tool depends, of course, upon the availability of equipment, budgetary considerations, and the use to which the tool can be put.

The authors have prepared this text in a form that will permit the chief of police, after reading this introductory chapter, to appoint subordinates to explore the feasibility of this medium for adoption by his department.

Budgetary considerations can be met depending on the size of the department and the availability of personnel. An important comparison to be made here is that of the cost factor in the use of video tape productions as opposed to both 16mm and 8mm film productions.

The psychology of the use of television excites both the sense of sight and the sense of hearing. Further, it involves the *participation* of the personnel, resulting in the identification of the officers with the program, to an extent not possible in film presentations.

Studies made in the educational field by staff psychologists reveal some startling statistics on the process of learning. Retention testing indicates that the normal person remembers 25 per cent of the information he *hears,* 55 per cent of what he *sees* and *reads,* and 65 per cent of what he *hears* and *sees.*

There are six general areas of application for the use of TV as a tool: administration, intelligence, surveillance, training, security, and prosecution.

ADMINISTRATION

How can TV be utilized within the framework of the police administrative setup? How can the police administrator use this tool?

In any department there exists the continual problem of clear and immediate communication downward along the hierarchical chain. Getting the "word" from the chief to the working level of patrolman is consistently difficult.

The problem of interpretation affects (and often modifies or changes) the "word." This occurs at the various staff and command levels through which the message, of necessity, must pass. The "word" is subject to the interpretation at each supervisory level; this may be done consciously or unconsciously, but it is done.

The sergeant or lieutenant affects the chief's wishes, whether they were originally expressed verbally or in writing. The sergeant affects the meaning of the chief's statement by his own interpretation, or lack of it, as well as by his prejudices. The prejudices may be conscious or unconscious. The very expression on the sergeant's face, and/or the intonation of his voice can and does affect the message he relays.

When the chief has a message for his people, why should he not deliver it in person? The answer is obvious: he would not normally go the twenty-four hours without sleep, which his appearance before three watches (in his station as well as in the various district stations, where they exist) would require.

How then does the chief avoid having his message reach the working patrolmen in a version that is watered down, if not completely misinterpreted?

He can in fact visit the roll call, thrice daily, and in the district stations, in person. He does this through the employment of video tape recording (VTR). He is recorded. He reviews the presentation to ascertain that he has indeed conveyed the message of his choice. The production is played at the various roll calls. Any errors or omissions are, of course, his own; suffice it to say that the message is not, as received by the officers, watered down or overinterpreted in the telling.

INTELLIGENCE

In the area of intelligence, VTR can be utilized in several ways. We will discuss a few of those ways.

Traffic problems can be covered by the VTR crew. A tape can be made, and the problem can be viewed at convenient times by the police traffic expert, the engineer, and others. The reviewing group can thus go about its normal business and have the problem brought to them for perusal and decision.

Prisoners can be taped during booking; the tape is later shown at roll calls, supplanting a formal showup, to acquaint all officers with those persons being arrested.

During the 1964 Republican Convention at Daly City's Cow Palace, Chief Roland Petrocchi implemented crowd surveillance by using moving picture cameras. The film could have been used for either, or both, intelligence or evidentiary purposes should the extent of the demonstrations have called for it. Happily, the demonstrations did not go that far. If the convention had been held at that location in 1968 or later, the moving picture cameras would have been supplanted by VTR. Several advantages would have resulted:

1. The officers working VTR know immediately what they have on film. It is unnecessary to spend time and money for processing.

2. If a VTR film lends itself to further training, it can easily be converted to motion picture film.

3. Normally, when VTR tape is no longer pertinent, it can be erased and used over again. The projected figure of reuse for the tapes is five hundred times. Even one hundred reuses would prove the value of VTR over motion picture film.

Thus, the VTR has all of the advantages of motion picture film, plus additional advantages (immediacy and reuse), with none of the disadvantages.

SURVEILLANCE

Surveillance of a store or bank in a "stakeout" situation, in anticipation of a robbery or burglary, can be much enhanced by VTR. The recent federal bank security moves might well be enhanced by use of the VTR, in lieu of the motion picture camera.

Supervision of surveillance can be aided by use of a remote VTR monitor; the supervisor need not be actually present at the scene of a fixed or moving surveillance in order to be continually appraised of the happenings.

During 1968, the city hall complex in Daly City was picketed daily for a two-week period. In a top-floor office a VTR camera was positioned and manned. Continual surveillance of the pickets was maintained. Taping could be started immediately upon the occurrence of a disturbance, or the threat of one. The resulting tapes could have been utilized (although it proved unnecessary) for intelligence and/or prosecutive purposes.

SECURITY

As with bank surveillance, jail security can be enhanced by VTR. The Daly City Police Department controls cells and prisoners by means of fixed VTR cameras. This allows dispatchers to perform a double function; they actually replace the need for physical presence of a policeman in the cell block on a permanent basis.

VTR can "watch" remote areas of civil buildings or complexes, particularly at night, on weekends, and on holidays, when all but police facilities are closed.

PROSECUTION

Any case in which film or tape recordings might be introduced as evidence lends itself to VTR; the scene is thereby brought directly before the jury. Where and when this is admissible, VTR is by far the best tool for such communication.

All of the arguments pertaining to crowd control, security, and surveillance apply to prosecution. Additionally, the cost factor again applies. VTR tape can be erased and reused when and where the pictures are not pertinent, or when they become dated.

Those departments currently utilizing motion pictures for drunken driver sobriety tests can utilize VTR much more cheaply and efficaciously than heretofore.

TRAINING OF PERSONNEL

Television generally, and VTR specifically, adapts superbly to various of the training areas. Such areas include, but are not limited to, recording of lectures, practical problems (such as booking procedures and accident investigations, use of the gas mask, field work by special groups, and introduction of the observations and thoughts of "outside experts" (who may be for the police, against them; or neutral).

We tried to hold to the concept that each team member should be able to do any job on the team. For field situations it is only necessary to have one or two cameramen. For the staged training sequence, it is also necessary to have a director, prop man, and lighting man, as well as others.

As nearly as was possible we selected members from each platoon and detail for two teams, so that hopefully there would always be a nucleus of personnel trained and ready to function on short notice. These men, as well as additional personnel, were taught to operate VTR equipment, so that training sequences could be played back to all watches around the clock.

We further utilized randomly selected officers from the department to "star" in various of the training sequences. Policemen are normally both aggressive and outgoing. Once the initial camera shyness was overcome, and with proper direction, all of those men selected performed like old troupers.

They were, importantly, natural before the camera. It was equally important that they not be too polished, for the policeman-viewer at roll call would then be unable to identify with them. Patrolmen were utilized mostly in the training sequence, just for the purpose of this identification. When a "message" was put on the VTR, of course, the services of the chief or a member of his staff were utilized.

Outside experts from other fields, such as the news media and the mental health field, were well received by the policemen-viewers.

Field training sequences were particularly successful. One example: During an extended riot control field exercise, with VTR obviously present, the participating officers performed very well. There was no horseplay, and while no one obviously played to the camera, all participants performed with great seriousness and effort. Later, they viewed themselves on playback. People like to see themselves on film, and these men were no exception. Thus, they identified with the program, and they had the advantage of the training first by participating, and second by viewing that participation.

EQUIPMENT

Once the program is "sold," and the funds for the equipment set aside, the actual purchase of the equipment must be considered. Even though, at this point, those in charge of the program will be eager to get the show on the road, this is the place to move very deliberately.

The purchasing department is advised to contact as many vendors as possible in the geographical area in which it is dealing. A small area (or a very large purchase) is recommended, so that necessary servicing and repair of the equipment can be conveniently implemented.

We recommend that the team of men designated to utilize the

equipment be present for all demonstrations and testings. If the selection is part of their doing, the personnel will identify with the equipment and the program; they are the people who will have to work with it and be satisfied with it.

SELECTION OF PERSONNEL

There are many ways in which specialized personnel can be selected for such a task. We will discuss here the procedure that proved sucessful for the Daly City Police Department.

In searching our "skills file," we were able to locate those personnel who had past employment or hobbies that would lend themselves to the VTR program. We also screened volunteers. In the beginning we familiarized and trained the men who had exhibited interest and who met the necessary requirements.

' Because ours is a seventy-man department, much of the work had to be on a voluntary basis, at least at the beginning of the program. The response of the men was gratifying. Those who stayed with the program were formed into two teams, which were later utilized in the filming of training and field situation sequences.

We found that we were able to progress through the stages from enthusiastic amateur to quasi-professional.

We learned, too, that the VTR program is limited only by the imagination of those using it, and that imagination was abundant among the team members.

This imagination has afforded a considerable impetus to the public relations program. Team members and their equipment accompany designated speakers to many speaking engagements. Having previously surveyed the scene of the impending talk to a public group, the team arrives early and sets up TV monitors and tape decks. When the speaker performs, he has the VTR visual aids present and functioning.

Taped programs can be made specifically for such presentations, or training films (where they are appropriate and not restricted) can be and have been employed. Public reception and acceptance of this portion of the program has been outstanding.

VTR is a valuable and practical police tool. It has proved useful in *our* department. We think it can be utilized in *your* department.

II

ADMINISTRATION

I N order to administer his department, the chief of police needs to communicate through his subordinate supervisors to all areas of his command. Policies and procedures, as articulated and set by the chief, are for the most part implemented by bureaus, divisions, details, and individual patrolmen.

There are those who say "write it down." This implies that the written word is a complete means of communication. The written word, in fact, is often used as a documentation. The documentations is used to show, should the occasion arise, that positive action was in fact taken on some issue. This in turn can serve as a defense for a chief who is under fire from the news media or other sources.

Such written evidence may also be the case of the future. If the recruit policeman is instructed on the gun policy of the department, often this is documented and the documentation is entered in the officer's record book. This may become the basis for future changes to be filed against the officer at the personnel, administrative, or criminal level in the case of an unfortunate misuse of a firearm.

The word *sanction* can mean that the chief condones, allows, or approves of certain actions taken by his commanders. Should he be displeased with the actions of his commanders, on the other hand, he might employ administrative sanctions in order to force compliance with the rules and regulations. Admittedly, the context in which the word is used is all-important; suffice it to mention here that the one word can convey opposite meanings.

Unfortunately, we see this confusion all the time in police reports, orders, memorandums, and guidelines. Homonyms are employed; the words sound alike but mean something different. The writer of the order may have made a simple mistake or misuse of the word; the test is the import that the word has upon the reader. This is not only important; it is vital. If the writer has not communicated his true meaning to the reader, then both the writer and the reader have wasted their time in bad communication at best, and complete misdirection and misunderstanding at worst.

The substitution of the word *effect* for *affect* might not be important, or it might be very important. The test of all writing is whether the reader properly understands what the writer intended him to comprehend.

Then, too, there are many occasions when the chief sends out a written directive, and it is not read *by* the patrolmen, but *to* them. This becomes in effect verbal communication, of which more will be said in the following paragraphs.

The chief may decide, either by choice or by necessity, to issue verbal instructions to be conveyed down the hierarchical scale to the level where implementation should occur. When he does this the import of his message may or may not get down to the working level of policemen, assuming that is where it was intended to go. His words will never be received by the men in their original context.

People change wording. This occurs because of speaking mannerisms, breadth or limitation of vocabulary, lazy listening, misunderstanding, or plain maliciousness and undercutting.

Words mean different things to different people. Many of us will have played the old Boy Scout word game. Sitting around the campfire at night, in a circle, the scout leader would whisper a message into the ear of the first boy. He in turn would repeat the message to his neighbor, and so on around the circle and into the ear of the last boy. It was the task of the last boy to repeat aloud the message which he had received. The leader would then recite the original message. The two never matched up completely, and sometimes were entirely different. The story, in effect, had altered in the telling.

Another such anecdote might assist us in viewing this problem. It might be appropriate also because it has been seen many times and by millions of people on commercial television late night shows. This is the situation where the master of ceremonies has as his panel of guests a number of multilingual persons. He tells a joke in English to the first person; none of the others can hear it, though the audience can. The first person then tells the joke in, perhaps, Spanish, to his nearest companion, who repeats the same joke in Italian to his next neighbor. The joke is conveyed around the table in German, then French, and so on. The last multilingual person receives the joke in another language.

Then he, like the last Boy Scout at the campfire, repeats the joke in English. Again, because of the translations (this is a key word, for we all interpret and translate) and nuances, the story does not match, and sometimes does not resemble the original. Again, the tale has suffered in the telling.

In both instances we can assume that each person in the communication circle sincerely did his best to communicate. Now let us assume the opposite. The sergeant receives a written or verbal order with which he decidedly disagrees. The order may be good or bad; this is not important. The important fact is that he disagrees.

The sergeant can actively destroy the significance of the order by saying, "Well, men, here it is. I don't agree with it, but this is what they want." What are the chances of that order being effectively carried out?

The sergeant, of course, in his disagreement with the directive, has taken a chance. He could have been less direct in his subversion. He could have read the order in a monotone, in a disinterested voice, word for word, and closed out without answering questions. This undermines the order as effectively, and less dangerously for him, as in the first instance. The expression on the sergeant's face, perhaps a curl of the lip, will also do damage.

A simple misunderstanding on the part of the sergeant can also do the job of destruction. If, for example, he has not properly prepared his roll call session, he may be reading the order for the first time when he reads it aloud to the assembled officers. This, of course, is readily apparent to the officers. They will not attach importance or credence to anything handled in so unprepared, slovenly, or ineffective a manner.

We have spoken of the misinterpreted verbal order, which becomes damaged or destroyed in the telling. We have mentioned the problems with written orders. At times, as we have seen, what starts out as a written order becomes verbal in the final dissemination to the men. All of these paths of communication have many pitfalls, as we have seen.

How, then, can the chief of police properly and effectively communicate his wishes and policies to the troops? The answer is simple. He can visit each watch, detail, division, and precinct station at roll call hour around the clock and personally tell them. This does not circumvent chain-of-command procedures so long as the subordinate police leaders are present. The chief may want to employ this method for separate and semiprivate meetings of sergeants, lieutenants, detectives, and the like.

The efficaceous implementation of this simple solution to the complex problem is something else again. Normally the chief does not make such visits, save for routine inspections, because of basic limitations. He is one man with a number of places to go. He must either be awake around the clock in order to visit all watches (in a medium-sized department), or he must take several days to make all stops in a larger department.

Should the chief of police be faced with this latter alternative, he will face a further and twofold problem. There will be an ineluctable delay in his message transmission, from his first to his last stop, which will cause a slow-motion sequence of communication. He will also find, as he progresses, for example, from one precinct station to another, that he and his message will have been preceded and subverted by wildfire rumor, replete with innuendo, misinterpretation, and premature critiques. At the very best he will find that the impact of his message has been greatly diminished.

This is the problem: How can the chief reach the most people in all units most effectively in the shortest period of time? The answer: He delivers his message in person by appearing and speaking on video tape.

Every good administrator will review his written order, and will have his administrative aides do the same. They will endeavor to discover the arguments against it. If the message holds up under evaluation and discussion, the chief will sign the order.

When the order is given on video tape, the chief and his aides have the opportunity to view it immediately, to criticize it, and perhaps, to re-do it. Ultimately, the chief's "signature" is his release for showing of the tape that to this point has been under his direct and sole control.

It is now possible for the chief to "visit" his precinct stations. At roll call the men watch him on the station monitor, listen to his message, watch his delivery, and, generally, "get the word." Perhaps one of the most important parts of the bridge between the communicator (chief) and communicant (patrolman) is the true import of the message as conveyed by the chief's vocal intonations and facial expressions. Where the dissident or ill-prepared patrol supervisor might have negated the message by the same means, The chief can employ them to the advantage of proper and efficient communication.

It is possible that the chief may be giving an ill-conceived order, or he may be giving a good order in an ineffective manner. If he does this, at least the "bad" order that results is in his own words; no one has misconstrued, misinterpreted, or otherwise blocked or harmed the intended communication.

Should the chief find that he does not have stage presence, he may utilize other methods. One that comes to mind is for him to select an administrative aide, perhaps a patrolman or sergeant, to stand in for him. This should be a man with whom the audience can readily identify. Having been thoroughly briefed, this officer can project the chief's thoughts, saying that he speaks for the chief. To lend credence and stature to the message, the chief can stand at the aide's elbow during the communication.

When it has been taped, the order is beamed to a district station or detail via closed circuit television. In the medium-sized department, it is a simple matter to cause the tape to be played on the monitor at roll call three times daily, for whatever period is necessary to reach all officers.

If the message lends itself to it, and if it is of sufficient import, the viewing can be implemented over educational or commercial television. In this fashion, the citizens are made aware of crucial policies that will have an effect on the community at large.

In all cases, the man with the message is giving that message directly to his audience. The lines of communication are shortened. The pitfalls are circumvented. The message is immediate. The order or directive is given.

We have spoken of the chief's video message as being an order. This is pertinent and realistic, but not all-inclusive. There are other messages that are readily and realistically adaptable to VTR.

Let us consider: The modern technical proficiency of commercial communication allows the President of the United States to enter our homes via the television screen. He comes to our homes for several reasons, one of which is pertinent to this writing. He is there in order to speak with us personally, or almost so, for obviously we cannot talk back to him. But he can and does talk to us in his own words, to personally convey a message directly to his public.

In spite of the fact that his talk will be dissected and interpreted in tomorrow's newspapers or in tonight's commentary, the President has spoken to the people. He has, on a much magnified scale, accomplished the same mission as has the chief of police who has communicated by closed circuit TV with the personnel in the district stations.

By this method the President has also made us all aware that he is a person, a human being, and an individual who can smile, joke, or be serious. His is a personal presentation, allowing us to view him as a man like ourselves.

So it can be with the chief of police. We have mentioned that he can give orders to his people in a direct manner in this fashion. He can also communicate other and, possibly, more positive messages to his department. This can be accomplished in much the same fashion as is done by the President. The only difference is in the size and location of the audience; the President speaks to millions in their homes, while the chief speaks to fewer people in the station houses. The efforts, goals, and results are very similar; in the chief's case, he will give occasional important orders or policy statements. He will not, of course, speak on every minimal item that might come to his attention or have to be decided by him, for he would be over-exposed and his message impact would be lessened.

The chief must try to do positive things in this approach where he, in fact, visits with his men. He will have periodic promotions and commendations to announce. When video taping promotions and high commendations, the chief should have the recipient officers present with him to be viewed on the screen by their fellows. Transfers (where they can be presented favorably and positively) and lesser commendations can merely be announced by the chief directly, without the officers concerned being present.

A former President's "fireside chats" encouraged a nation in difficult days. He spoke directly to the people and they responded to this, then, novel approach. The chief can likewise personally visit his officers, not only to set out orders and policies, but to commend, promote, and encourage. Among other things, administration and leadership is concerned with morale; video tape recordings are a means to this end.

III

INTELLIGENCE

THE role of the police department as an intelligence-gathering agency is becoming increasingly more important. With the periodic upsurge of radical movements and their peripheral followers, and the ever-increasing exchange of law enforcement information because of the mobility of the criminal, it is necessary for even the modestly sized police organization to have an intelligence-gathering unit, be it one man or many. Intelligence is an expensive function for larger departments, with many budget dollars expended for the filming of important meetings and gatherings of suspects. Many of these budget dollars go down the drain when after several hours of filming, a meeting or gathering does not occur or take the turn that it was supposed to. If video tape has been used, since it can be reused, the only real loss is in time and manpower.

Aside from the more sophisticated intelligence work, there are day-to-day areas of intelligence that must be covered. For this, television is an important tool, along with the microphone, camera, and tape recorder.

TRAFFIC CONTROL

Every municipality has a "problem intersection" or a location that is badly engineered. This is a frequent headache to the police administrator. A fixed television camera can be assigned to this area or intersection and put into operation at the time or times that are most necessary (Fig. 1). An operator may or may not be present;

Figure 1. The cameraman uses a cherry picker for a better vantage point from which to study a traffic situation. *(DCPD photograph)*

he can set up the equipment, leave, and return to change the tapes, then bring the full tape back to headquarters. A group of traffic experts or engineers, or department administrative heads, can objectively view the area and decide what, if any, changes will have to be made. This enables the department to make necessary realignments based on the graphic portrayal of the problem. The tapes can be played several times, if necessary, and discussed from every aspect before any changes are instituted. With the completion of the changes and the solution, another survey with the equipment can be made to insure that the new pattern functions smoothly. Such a situation is now being undertaken by a State Police agency in the Southwest in cooperation with the federal government. On a particularly "accident-prone" area of the state freeway system, television cameras have been installed; the pictures are broadcast to a monitoring station, as well as being video taped for further study. From this, the "accident-free" highway of the future may be designed, and corrective measures found to eliminate the hazards of today. Smaller departments may not be able to avail themselves of the broadcast features, but they can now use the closed circuit equipment to its fullest extent.

CROWD CONTROL

Every police supervisor experiences at one time or another the problem of crowd control. Even the friendliest and most well-meaning of large gatherings can be only minutes away from a riot triggered by some minor incident that occurs inside the crowd. If they are not quickly contained and isolated, minor disturbances can escalate into violence and injury. Police practice is to station patrolmen and plain-clothesmen in key areas to prevent a friendly crowd from erupting into an unruly mob. In most cases this is effective. But nearly all supervisors breathe a sigh of undisguised relief when the event is finally concluded and the participants are safely on their way home.

Planning for such an event should include the use of one or two television cameras in fixed positions selected in advance, preferably, and in such a location as to view the general areas of the gathering. It may even be necessary to move the cameras to several locatons during the event, to follow the movement of the crowd (Fig. 2). These cameras can feed into one or two monitors at a predesignated

Figure 2. The cameraman "shoots" a crowd of people attending a Cow Palace event. *(DCPD photograph)*

location that remains constant. The overall supervisor can establish this as his command post and guide the activities of his officers from this location.

With this visual arrangement, the police supervisor follows the crowd without appearing to be too obvious and can guide his men to the right spot at the right time with a minimum of confusion. If it becomes necessary to remove a solitary troublemaker from an event, the supervisor can judge the response needed and send the proper number of men to the spot; he can guide their actions while still keeping a watchful eye on the rest of the crowd to gauge their tone and mood.

A practical example of the advantages of the television-augmented command post is our experience at the 1964 Republican Convention at the Cow Palace in Daly City. This was before our department adopted television. It is, in fact, one of the reasons the chief of police decided to request the equipment in his budget.

As is the case with all major political conventions, the commercial broadcasters spent hundreds of thousands of dollars in preparing for the convention coverage. In the trailer command post at the Cow Palace, several televsion monitors were provided for the chief of police and his staff to view the activities in and around the Convention. From this site, and taking advantage of the expansive network coverage, the chief was able to maintain tight control on the police activities and was able to sense problems before they occurred. As particular posts were supplemented, the chief was able to provide additional manpower instantly from less sensitive areas. If necessary, he could respond to the problem himself. Subordinates still in the command post were able to keep him current on other areas that might need additional manpower. It was for this reason that we were able to handle a crowd of some *fifty thousand* people daily using less than three hundred policemen.

RIOT CONTROL

This subject follows crowd control as night must surely follow day. When positive measures to constrain a crowd fail, or when a riot occurs with no warning, then action must be taken. Again, the effective police supervisor must have the best possible intelligence on the mob and their activities so that he may deal with them correctly (Fig. 3). A word of caution: When the intelligence to be gathered is of an unruly group or mob, some care must be given to the identification of the equipment operators, or rather, to the lack of any identifying uniform or marked equipment. Rioters are quick to sense that television can be used as a form of prosecution evidence against them.

Whether the camera operators are policemen or commercial broadcasters seems to make little difference in the mind of the faceless rioter, who will take every step necessary to preserve his anonymity. Care should be taken to place the cameras and the operators in a position to cover the area while still insuring their physical safety. This can be done with the use of long-range lenses (see Chapter X).

In recent times, much has been made of the use of the subpoena to impound as possible evidence audio and visual records made by radio and television groups at riot scenes. A further discussion of this will be undertaken in Chapter VII. In this chapter we will deal not

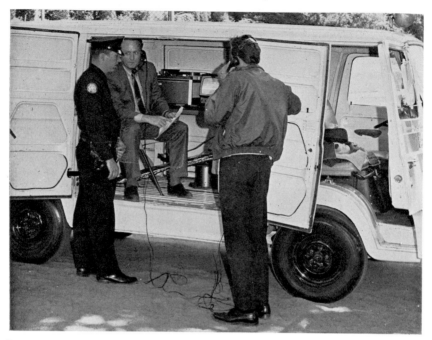

Figure 3. The van can be utilized for training purposes, or, as in this case, as a riot control command post. *(DCPD photograph)*

with the broad area of prosecution but with the specific methods of gathering intelligence.

HIGH CRIME AREAS

Every city has areas that by peculiar makeup have high crime rates. Burglaries occur in the business districts during the early-morning hours, in the exclusive residential areas during the day, and in high-rise apartment building around the clock. There are certain streets within the city that may have a prevalent vice problem, such as prostitution, numbers running, bookmaking, or traffic in narcotics. Personal surveillances by specialized vice or crime units are in order, but as is generally the case, the criminal is quick to spot the stranger and identify him as the police. These criminal types are spoken of as "being paranoid," and so they are. Their nefarious activities are best performed away from the prying eyes of the police.

Sub rosa surveillances are often undertaken, and from this intelligence a plan of attack is formulated by the concerned police unit. Frequently, 16mm films are made for this purpose. Our proposal is that video tape equipment be used for this, for more taping can be done with less expense and more effective results. Television monitoring of areas with high burglary rates could be undertaken for several days and repetitive "faces" would quickly be isolated in the area. Monitoring entrances to and from high-rise apartment buildings could identify tenants, service personnel, and professional burglars. Narcotics dealers could be identified and singled out and their pattern could be studied by the undercover officer prior to any physical contact. The same would apply to the streetwalker and her prospective client.

The application of television equipment described in the preceding paragraphs differs slightly from that of detective surveillance, which will be covered in the next chapter. Intelligence observations do not always result in arrests and therefore should be construed for the purposes of this chapter as merely the gathering of information and its dissemination to the appropriate police unit.

Intelligence gathering is a continuing task; the fruits of the intelligence may be divided and sent to several different units or details for follow-up work. The crew that does the actual video taping may be from the Intelligence Unit, Special Services Bureau, or it may consist of assigned officers from the Patrol Division. The equipment used is simple to master and can be used by all units or divisions within the department with much less work than is required to train an operator of an 8mm or 16mm camera. With instant viewing and instant replay added, it becomes virtually impossible for the operator to make any mistakes; immediate correction is possible for any that might occur.

Should any tapes be of importance, they can be set aside and retained for future reference. If they contain little of value, they can be reused on subsequent occasions, as opposed to the more costly expedient of having to film, process, view, and then store all films made with a standard movie camera.

Departments, large and small, may be called upon to record gatherings of radical, revolutionary, subversive, or militant movements. These may be outdoor rallies or demonstrations. They could be meetings in clubs or members' residences. Filming by video tape can be from fixed posts in dwellings, vans, or even automobiles.

Participants can be video taped and the tape returned immediately to headquarters, ready instantly for viewing by members of the staff who may have to deal with these persons at a later time.

This type of surveillance takes a minimum of personnel and limits the knowledge of the existence of the tapes to a restricted number, established by the chief, who have access to this sensitive information.

IV

SURVEILLANCE BY DETECTIVE DIVISIONS

ONE of the key missions of the criminal investigation unit is preparing cases for prosecution. Every incident that becomes a crime, and that ultimately leads to the arrest of a defendant or defendants, requires solid facts. In developing cases, the detective uses many or all of the tools of crime detection that are available to him. With the onslaught of new precedents in the area of criminal justice, investigators are becoming increasingly aware of the necessity of presenting the best possible evidence to the prosecutor and the courts.

More and more, use is being made of such augmentations as the tape recorder and the camera in securing admissible evidence to insure a successful conviction. In many cases the detective must spend long hours on fruitless stakeouts waiting for the "break" that will turn the tide in his favor.

Throughout these writings we stress the immediacy of the television camera for recording events that can never be restaged. The most critical of these events is the crime or the crime scene. Obviously, the criminal will not reconstruct the crime, nor will the courts permit him to. For in a reconstruction, the emotion of the moment is lost. Juries viewing such a charade would be quick to spot the theatrical atmosphere under which such an event was made and would infer that some undue pressure had been brought to bear on the defendant.

In viewing the crime without the augmentation of television, the investigator, who is a trained observer, must attempt to re-create verbally in the courtroom the original situation. Judges and juries generally want to believe the policeman on the stand and pay close attention to the testimony of such an expert witness. They also listen to and observe the defendant in the courtroom. How do we convince the jury that the defendant did, in fact, commit the crime?

By taking advantage of the video tape unit, the detective can use the camera and record the surveillance with little prior experience. When the opportune moment arises, he will be prepared to record the criminal act that is his reason for being on the stakeout. Most video cameras are easily adapted to the addition of long-range lenses and may be coupled with such audio innovations as the "shotgun" microphone or the FM wireless microphone. With this combination, the detective can be in a covert position some distance away from the scene itself, and yet still record, accurately and immediately, the action as it progresses.

A typical surveillance arrangement is pictured in Figure 4. In it, a detective operator is viewing and simultaneously filming a crime as it transpires. From his hidden vantage point, the detective can, by radio, guide his partners to the scene at the proper moment. When they arrive, the operator can continue his filming and record the climate under which the defendant was advised of his rights. The judge and jury would then be in a position to decide whether or not an intelligent waiver had, in fact, been made. Should there be any

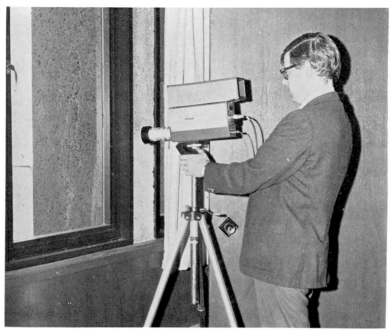

Figure 4. Surveillance camera with zoom lens is operated from a top-story city hall office. Pickets were the focus of the surveillance for both prosecutive and intelligence purposes. *(DCPD photograph)*

physical resistance to the arrest, that would also be recorded and built-in protection would be assured against any future charges of police intimidation or brutality.

With the use of video tape equipment, surveillances do not necessarily require that an operator be present under all circumstances. If a problem exists, for example, in a particular area of a large department store that is experiencing losses, taped monitoring may be of value in pinpointing the time and/or the culprit. Figures 5 and 6 depict an area under surveillance. It is not necessary with a fixed-camera operation to keep the detective operator always present; periodic visits to the monitoring station to change the tapes are sufficient. Running the completed tape allows the detective to view the tape at his leisure. By using the fast-forward mode he can bypass those points of the tape that are of no significance to him. When the investigator finds the incriminating portion of the tape, he merely

Figure 5. Monitor in security office of a large department store. *(DCPD photograph)*

Figure 6. Mounted surveillance camera in a large department store. *(DCPD photograph)*

Figure 7. Surveillance camera in a busy shop. *(Courtesy of Harman's Kentucky Fried Chicken)*

has to identify the employee responsible, who generally, when confronted with the damning evidence, will present the investigator with the entire account of his transgressions with little or no prompting (Figs. 7 and 8).

There is also available a simple self-contained unit which can either be used covertly or, in the case of loss prevention, overtly, and which serves the same purpose (Fig. 9). This unit is further described in Chapter X.

HOMICIDE AND DEATH INVESTIGATIONS

Video taping homicide scenes with the battery pack camera to infuse new blood into routine investigations provides the detective with a permanent and vivid portrayal of the scene as it was when the crime was discovered.

The scene will never be the same. Metaphysically, it is impossible

Figure 8. Surveillance camera in a busy shop. *(Courtesy of Harman's Kentucky Fried Chicken)*

Figure 9. Sony's new EV-330TLV time lapse video tape recorder *(Sony Corporation)*

to re-create it. even if were possible, the emotionally charged atmosphere could not be recaptured.

Objective viewing by the homicide investigator as an adjunct to his follow-up may give him a new perspective.

No matter how accurate and complete his notebook, it is difficult for the investigator to record the nuances of the verbal language. Subtle changes in inflection or emphasis, and lanugage difficulties by the witness or suspect, are permanently recorded on video tape. Background activity, possibly very important, is peripherally recorded for the busy investigator's later perusal.

Video tape also permits the detail commander to review and appraise the activity of the "on the scene" detective and technicians, and can prove to be a valuable method of bringing into the courtroom the actual crime scene and interviews with witnesses as they actually took place.

After the courtroom proceedings and the period for appeal are over, the video tapes are transmitted to the Training Division for possible usc in giving recruit officers a first-hand working knowledge of the typical homicide scene (see Chapter V).

ROBBERY INVESTIGATIONS

Many times during his career, the investigator will be called upon to stake out the potential site of a robbery. Care is always given to the spot from which the observation is to be made. Some instances require that the potential victim be kept unaware that such a task is under way. Attention is given to the physical well-being of the officers involved as well as to innocent parties in the area. Strategically located cameras with long-range lenses provide the detective with the ideal surveillance location. He then uses a minimum of personnel and has greater flexibility in making necessary and immediate changes in his plans.

Installation of self-contained units in businesses that are constantly plagued with the potential of robbery has sharply curtailed the number of robberies attempted (see Chapter VI).

BURGLARY INVESTIGATIONS

There are opportunities for even greater flexibility in the areas of breaking and entering, since the burglar is at work almost around the clock. We have already briefly discussed the area of burglary surveillance in Chapter III and will now expand upon the possibilities. Burglaries are generally classified as residential, commercial, nighttime, daytime, roof, apartment, automobile, warehouse, and loft. The imaginative investigator who is aware of the uses of video tape equipment can have a more successful career than his burglarizing adversary by taking advantage of the modern techniques. Burglars, like most recidivists, make the mistake of falling into a pattern, or *modus operandi,* and the good investigator takes advantage of this.

Knowing the equipment that is available and properly deploying it can put the burglary detective in more than one spot at any given time. He then is able to screen the tapes and probably can spot his man without letting this advantage be known. The key to solving nearly every burglary rests in the identification of the suspect. From that point, routine investigative procedures make it an easy "grab" for the burglary officer.

SEX CRIMES

Most investigations of sex offenses committed against young children are hampered by the lack of a good description of the suspect and his automobile. Here again, the investigator assigned to the sex crime detail can use television and his imagination to his advantage. The majority of these crimes occur at obvious locations. The sex crime offender spends much of his time at schools, parks, or playgrounds. The technique is the same. Periodic surveillance by television can show us who else is watching the playgrounds.

AUTO THEFT INVESTIGATIONS

Automobile larcenies are an ever-present problem to police departments. Many of the offenders are young joyriding juveniles who steal automobiles for their personal use, then abandon them when they are done or when they run out of gas. Large parking lots surrounding business areas, shopping centers, or airports are frequent targets for the joyrider, as well as for the professional car thief. Generally, because of the size of these parking lots and the lack of sufficient available manpower, it is nearly impossible for police departments to give these situations the attention they need.

The citizen, when he finds that his automobile has been stolen, expects a policeman to recover his car. The law enforcement officer is more concerned with the prevention of auto theft.

Television equipment can be utilized to a much larger degree and can give the police administrator what he would like to have, a policeman covering many areas at the same time. If the problem exists in a large parking lot, as an example, there is one advantage to the police. Parking lots have limited exits, and camera surveillance of these spots can be centralized to one monitoring position, where one officer can be scanning several monitors simultaneously. If the monitor shows some unusual or suspicious activity, the officer is then in a position to send a mobile unit to respond and make further inquiries as to the circumstances.

VICE CONTROL AND INVESTIGATIONS

While this function does not generally come under the heading of the criminal investigation division, we will treat it as such for the purpose of furthering our discussion of the surveillance possibilities of television.

In Chapter III we discussed the intelligence that can be gathered in the area of vice control; now we will deal with the reduction of the problem by investigative means.

Narcotics cases require keen and alert investigators. The dealer in narcotics or other dangerous drugs is fast-moving, keenly alert to possible observation, and stealthy by nature. This, in turn, tends to sharpen the wits of the narcotics officer, who may take advantage of every possible means of legally and successfully bringing about the peddler's downfall. The narcotics officer is usually highly imaginative and will be quick to grasp the significant contribution that video tape can play in the completion of his mission.

The same can also be said for the investigator assigned to the prostitution and gambling squads. By the very nature of the crimes involved, a patient, well-thought-out, and exacting case is required to bring the transgressor into the courtroom.

It has been our experience that the Vice Control Unit makes more use of specialized devices than most other police details. Investment in television equipment to be placed in the hands of the Vice Control Unit alone should reap highly profitable rewards.

V

TRAINING

T HE video tape recorder is the greatest training tool to come along since the invention of the motion picture camera. Like the camera, VTR records real people and things and their voices and sounds in actual or contrived settings. Like motion picture filming the tape can then be utilized for portraying pertinent material to officers for training purposes.

Unlike the camera, VTR can do this instantly. With the camera, one needs to wait to develop the film, then to review it, and finally to edit it. With VTR one knows instantly what he has and its value.

It is readily recognized, then, that VTR has all of the advantages of the camera and none of the disadvantages, with a large plus added by its own unique features.

The video tape recorder is a combined movie camera and audio tape recorder enhanced by instant replay and economy. As mentioned elsewhere in these writings, the use of this tool is limited only by the imagination of the user. In this chapter we will discuss its uses within the training framework.

Pictorial and audio training is normally better received by officers than is the hoary lecture method. Supplemental lectures have value, but Confucius' adage about pictures being better than words remains true. Our figures show that the retention quotient of officers being trained is significantly higher for both movies and VTR than for any other classroom method.

VTR has been employed in defensive driving training. The officer being trained or retrained finds himself at the track in a specially equipped police car, accompanied by his instructor. Having been thoroughly briefed, and with all safety systems having been implemented, the officer goes for his ride.

In the front or back seat is a VTR operator, who records voice and automobile sounds and critically captures the driver's movements from within the automobile. A typical shot will view the driver from behind, showing him reacting to the commands of his trainer and manipulating the controls; through the windshield, it gives a driver's-eye view of the road and the obstacles being encountered. This recording is done with a battery pack camera.

Meanwhile, one or more cable VTR cameras operates in the field. These cameras record the movements of the vehicle from the outside, as they would be seen by anyone on the street.

Immediately following the ride, the trainee can view his movements and those of his vehicle from all angles. He can easily and immediately see what was done right and what was done wrong. Through this instant replay, the trainer and his driver can determine whether they should repeat the performance.

In the event that the performance has been a good one, the driver in effect has gone through the exercise twice—once when he actually drove the car, and the second time when he viewed and heard himself driving it.

For the training of other drivers, the VTR presentation can be repeated in the classroom, perhaps during the early indoctrination stage of this training (Fig. 10). In the classroom, the exterior and interior shots can be alternated to give the viewer the whole picture. Later, if the recording proves to be exceptionally valuable, it is a

Figure 10. Several departments represented at a riot control training class. Having performed in the field, they now view themselves on video tape. *(DCPD photograph)*

simple matter to convert it into motion picture film for more formalized training (see Chapter X).

Should the tape not prove to be valuable, it is easily erased. The tape can be used again and again. Clearly, the procedure is far less costly than that of the motion picture method, and is even more precious because of the immediacy of the results.

At any point in the proceedings, voice commentary by the trainer can be dubbed into the presentation tape in order to obtain or enhance continuity of instruction.

Tapes that have been taken for surveillance or evidentiary purposes can prove to be estimable training aids (see Chapter IV).

Once the tapes are no longer required as evidence, the case is closed or past appeal, or when other matters are no longer pertinent, the tape can and should be turned over to the Training Division. The instructors can decide whether the material lends itself to training. This should always be decided, first, by detectives as to which tapes to release, and second, by the trainers as to their viability as a current training aid.

Detectives must be the people to decide when their cases are finished. They then should always be required to route the tapes to the trainers. Detectives have cases on their minds, and in their busy schedule they should not have to determine training suitability. Once they have reviewed the tape, the training people can erase it if it is pertinent to training, or return it to the files for further use.

Again, should the training people judge the tape to be currently pertinent to training, they can schedule it to be viewed either at

Figure 11. At roll call, the new watch views a short training tape. (DCPD *photograph*)

roll call, time permitting, or in the recruit or retraining classroom situation (Fig. 11). Tapes of exceptional and long-lasting value can and should be converted to motion picture film.

An example of this last is the crime scene in a homicide investigation. A video tape recording of the scene itself, the actions of the investigators, the measurement taking, and the sketching and photographing, becomes an invaluable and always current training aid. One can even obtain the acts of witness interviewing and suspect warning and interrogation for the training effort (see Chapter IV). In such a matter, when the case is concluded, we have a sample for viewing that cannot possibly be re-created in the classroom by other means.

Some officers work for years before being exposed to an actual murder. In this fashion, every new and veteran officer has the scene brought to him. For all practical purposes, he has actually participated in the investigation.

Riot control training lends itself to VTR extremely well. Consider: In these days of dissent and disturbance, policemen must be trained to cope with crowds and mobs (see Chapter III). So we find that we must, at least occasionally, train the officers in groups and as a unit. Such training should include all policemen at times, and special units on a regular basis.

Video tape recording can play an important role for the very large department where the actual riot training of all patrolmen is an impracticality. Yet these officers may have to beef up the special unit or hold the line until the arrival of that unit. Assuming that training and discipline demand that all officers be in good physical condition, they need only know something of riot control techniques and basic formations. Video tape recordings of the special units in training or in actual situations, shown to a typical platoon of patrolmen, can supplant to some extent the actual field training of these generalist officers (Fig. 12).

VTR impressions taken at the scene of a disturbance should always be shown to the special units. Members of the units can then see themselves in action, and can criticize and improve their operation in the future.

VTR enhances the value of riot control training in a number of ways. To assemble a platoon, company, or class of policemen for

Figure 12. The cameraman records the anti-sniper team's exposure to chemical agents and the use of the gas mask. *(DCPD photograph)*

training purposes is very costly, save, possibly, at the recruit academy where the men are already assembled. All too often, unfortunately, such training is "extra," aside from normal duty hours and tours of duty. Even when officers can be reassigned to training (perhaps for a day), this means trimming the watches and details, which is in itself very costly.

These are all additional reasons for us to get the maximum results from such a training period. When the officers are assembled and taught, and then perform, we may have good training, but not maximum results.

Photography, motion picture or still, records such activities to advantage. The problem, again, is the time lag for development of the film, and then getting the film shown to the participants, who may be from scattered platoons, stations, and details.

Let us assume that we have assembled a company of policemen for a riot control training session. They have been lectured and have

Figure 13. Anti-sniper team members criticize their training, while being taped by a battery pack cameraman. Note the fixed camera in the background. *(DCPD photograph)*

observed pertinent films or recordings of other such training. Now they are assembled in an open area, riot-equipped and ready for the practical exercises.

The VTR team is also there. Cable cameras are positioned around and above the exercise area. A team member with a battery pack camera can perform with and around the unit (Fig. 13). The combined recording should show the unit from within, as if seen from the commander's eyes; it should show the unit from above, as a commentary on the actual close-order formations used; and it should show the unit from the side and in front, as the unit might be observed by adjacent police units and by the mob.

All phases of the training operation should be recorded. Good training includes allowing time for a critique. During this period, the officers are brought to the classroom, and the VTR is played back to them. This is an invaluable part of the training.

Most people think of themselves. Policemen are no different. Each will look first for himself, and then at the group. Each officer becomes his own critic and a critic of the group. Having performed the necessary evolutions, the officer, while physically at ease, visually and mentally performs the entire operation again. Commentary from the trainers will put matters into perspective.

We have now trained our group. They have performed physically. They have watched the performance from the viewpoint that others would have. They have "performed" twice, and have actually seen the good and the bad of their efforts. The use of VTR vis-à-vis the critique allows immediacy of viewing, of comment, of criticism and correction. The officers view their efforts while still "up" for the exercise mentally and while still perspiring physically; they are, in fact, still participating. Experience shows us, further, that participant comments are elicited and multiplied by VTR use.

There is yet a further advantage to the utilization of VTR coupled with riot control training. It seems that, once over their initial and natural shyness, the officers become used to performing for the eye. Thus, when the officers go to an actual riot scene, they are not overly shy of the cameras and TV, the press, or the other police already present.

As mob members relish the anonymity of the group, so do the officers prefer the relative anonymity of their group. It is axiomatic, however, that the news media will be present at a disturbance, and that the anonymity of the officer does not really exist. Having trained before VTR, the officers find that the media photographers and TV people, as well as the cameramen employed by the dissidents, hold no great danger for them.

The officer knows how he looks on film or tape. He knows what to do at the scene and how to follow orders. He knows from training where he has looked good and where he has not.

The VTR-trained officer now is conditioned to performing in a goldfish bowl. He is able to perform well. He is better able to avoid untoward or unfortunate actions that will cause him to appear on the front page of a newspaper in an unfortunate negative pose or provocative act.

As mentioned, the training of all specialized groups is enhanced by the use of VTR. In a training session of a police anti-sniper team,

Figure 14. The shotgun man provides the cameraman with material for a future training tape. *(DCPD photograph)*

Figure 15. The mechanics of shotgun firing are recorded by a battery pack camera for future training. *(DCPD photograph)*

for example, VTR is easily and profitably employed. We suggest that a VTR team member with battery pack accompany the police rifleman on his field exercises. Recording from the rear or side of the officer will show all of his actions. The classroom student can view the scene almost through the eyes of the police rifleman, while watching the mechanics of his movements (Figs. 14 and 15).

When the police rifleman is making a "dry run," i.e., not actually firing the rifle, but running through an operation for practice, a cable VTR should shoot from the standpoint and viewpoint of that officer's opponent. Thus, during the critique later before the monitor, the rifleman can judge his use of cover and concealment and his general method of operation. It is extremely enlightening and instructive to view oneself through the "eyes" of one's opponent.

We have mentioned elsewhere (Chapter II) how the chief of police can address his people through the apparatus of the VTR

Figure 16. The captain instructs on police-community relations and services. The performance is video taped for showing at the police roll call sessions. (*DCPD photograph*)

Figure 17. Abetted by a cooperative merchant, the crew stages an "arrest" situation for the camera. The resulting training tape was entitled *How To Talk to the Drunk*. *(DCPD photograph)*

arrangement (Fig. 16). The trainer can do likewise by preparing instructional presentations for utilization at roll call training or for other classroom situations (Figs. 17 and 18).

A particularly good class lecture or demonstration can be profitably employed for future classes. We suggest that great care be taken in selecting the people who will instruct via VTR. To have the chief or a supervisor appear too often as an instructor is a mistake. Generally, we will want to select an instructor with whom the audience of uniformed patrolmen can identify. In this way the audience is more likely to have greater retention of the subject matter presented to it.

In short, then, we suggest that most VTR instruction be carried out by a peer of the audience, in this case a sergeant or patrolman. Needless to say, the officer instructing on VTR needs to have

Figure 18. When "talking to the drunk" fails, an arrest is sometimes necessary. The resulting tapes showed both "right" and "wrong" arrest techniques. (*DCPD photograph*)

knowledge of his subject, stage presence, and the ability to communicate adequately. The officer need not, however, necessarily be a "collar ad" type, nor need he have the eloquence of a politician. In fact, these very attributes can negate the identification of the audience with the performer.

Panel discussions are helpful to the training effort. Representative department members, discussing practical police problems for VTR presentation, provide excellent training material. Again, it is possible for the viewer to identify with both the problem and the group discussion members. This training also smooths over some of the problems created by rigidly structured classroom settings, as well as allowing training impact to occur from within the ranks as opposed to continual edicts from the hierarchy of the department.

Not all training should come from within the department. Source people from the community can be invaluable to the training effort. Most persons, even the anti-establishment types, are happy to talk to policemen, and to express their views. It is good practice to put such people onto VTR for presentation to the officers. Where the speaker is anti-police, care should be taken to balance the comment by having a member of the department or a pro-police person talk to the same sitting.

A college professor can easily be utilized in his field, which could be physical evidence or sociology. A learned, concise, pragmatic discussion on trigger terms by a semanticist, conveyed on VTR, could be of great value to the viewing officers. Most professional types are happy to oblige with contributions from their field of concentration.

Much can be accomplished in the area of court testimony, demeanor, and case presentation. There are many ways of accomplishing this; let us mention one.

The training people arrange for a visit by (or to) three persons whose combined views cover the entire courtroom spectrum. They have each person talk for fifteen to twenty minutes on the subject.

The magistrate can give the overview of the courtroom as seen from the bench. The prosecutor will speak on preparation of the case, the pre-trial conference, and the officer's appearance and testimony. A cooperative defense lawyer might discourse on his philosophies and problems, such as why certain questions are asked on cross examination, how he has defeated officer witnesses, and how they have defeated him.

This can be recorded in one setting. The three speakers should probably converse for a while prior to going on tape. Then, one at a time, they are introduced to the VTR and give their presentations. The greater the stature of the participants, the greater is the value of their offerings, and the easier is the acceptance by the viewing officer.

We have gone into the community to obtain source persons for such presentations with noticeably good and acceptable results. One outstanding example was in the area of police relations with the news media. Mr. Ed Montgomery consented to speak on VTR for the edification of the officers. This Pulitzer Prize-winning investigative reporter rendered a valuable study of such relations as seen from his vantage point of thirty very successful years of newspaper work (Fig. 19).

A panel of policemen appeared with Mr. Montgomery on VTR, asking and discussing the questions most often asked by policemen concerning press relations.

An outline of the film was made as follows:

57 TRAINING 36C
COURSE TITLE: Community Relations
LESSON TITLE: Talk to the Press
INSTRUCTOR: Sergeant John Kolbmann
RUNNING TIME: 18 minutes
DATE FILMED: 7-26-68
DESCRIPTION:

This film is the first of two panel discussions on the subject of police relations with the press. In it, Mr. Ed Montgomery, a thirty-year veteran of newspaper work and presently in his twenty-fourth year with the *San Francisco Examiner,* talks with Lieutenant Thomas Culley and Officer Donald Horsley concerning the attitudes and actions of the police and journalists during periods of stress. Examples are given of problems encountered during recent riots in Oakland and San Francisco.

REFERENCES: DCPD SOP 35.50 Press Procedures

TECHNICAL INFORMATION:

This film was directed by Sergeant John Kolbmann, camera work by Officer John McHenry and audio-video handled by Technician Lucia. The following personnel appear in this segment: Captain Hansen introduces and closes the panel, which consists of Mr. Ed Montgomery, Lieutenant Thomas Culley, and Officer Donald Horsley.

FILMING TIME: Three hours (for both 36C and 36D).

REPORT DISTRIBUTION:

Original—Captain Hansen

2 copies—training file

7-28-68   0645   SGT. J. J. Kolbmann, #63

There are generally three areas into which VTR training tapes fall. The first area, as with the riot control effort, is for training, pure and simple. The second area is informational in nature, as with the panel

Figure 19. Mr. Ed Montgomery, Pulitzer Prize-winning investigative reporter for the *San Francisco Examiner,* holds a discussion with members of the department. The resulting informational tape was titled *Talk to the Press,* and was played to the officers at the various roll calls. *(DCPD photograph)*

discussion just mentioned. These programs consist for the most part of "off the record" comments which are restricted to departmental dissemination, and which are made with the condition that they not go out for public viewing.

The third area concerns the public. At times training tapes lend themselves to public viewing, in terms of police image enhancement, or are of informational value to portions of the public. Other such tapes can be made, aimed at the aspect of police public relations. Such tapes adapt admirably to PTA groups, service clubs, fraternal organizations and the like.

In all cases, the tapes are filmed, indexed, and retained as long as they are current and pertinent. When currency or pertinency dissolve with time, if they do, the tape is erased and reused. Where a tape is of exceptional quality, it can be transformed into a motion picture film for long-range retention and showing.

VI

SECURITY

S ECURITY has many meanings. Within the context of this chapter, it has a simple but important meaning. Keeping that which is to be protected under guard or the watchful eye. What better watchful eye than the lens of the television camera?

Security is a watchword in the police mission. As policemen, we are constantly called upon to guard or protect persons or property. Let us now discourse upon some ways of providing the maximum observation with the minimum expenditure of personnel and equipment.

INTERNAL POLICE PREMISES

Administrators are becoming increasingly aware of the possibility of entrance to the police structure, and of damage, theft, or sabotage to the building and occupants. It could scarcely be argued that, under most circumstances, it is necessary to post perimeter guards around the police complex. However, there are many times, given sufficient help, when it would be of great value to have men assigned to cover critical spots in the building. Losses are constantly reported from the personal possessions of the officers that are kept in the locker rooms. Under certain given circumstances, the bomb or arson threat must be considered (Fig. 20). Generally these threats follow some intensified police action against a group and when permitted the opportunity, they may come to fruition. Usually, every police station has a desk sergeant or officer on duty at a fixed location. This man could be given the peripheral duty of scanning the television monitors that could be placed at or near his position (Figs. 21 and 22). Remote control units are available on the market that provide extreme versatility in picture adjustment; he may move the camera or "zoom" in or out with the lens. The installation is not difficult or extremely complex and can be done by a police technician. Should it become necessary, relocation of the camera position is not a complex task and can be handled by personnel within the department.

EXTERNAL POLICE PREMISES

Entrance to the building itself is sometimes difficult, so the extremist may attempt to do his damage on the outside of the police structure (Fig. 23). Cameras may be installed as exterior guardians, monitored from within either by the desk officer or by personnel in the communications center (Fig. 24). These cameras also could be coupled with remote control units to provide full coverage under varying lighting conditions and could be rotated to insure the fullest observation possible.

Figure 20. Some of the results of the fatal bombing at San Francisco's Park Police Station. TV surveillance cameras were subsequently installed. *(San Francisco Examiner photograph)*

Figure 21. A San Francisco policeman, on security duty at the bombed Park Police Station, is able to tape record any happenings outside of the building. *(DCPD photograph)*

Figure 22. The interior of Park Station, showing the surveillance camera monitor. Note the bomb fragment damage. *(DCPD photograph)*

Figure 23. The aftermath of a bombing at the Berkeley, California, police parking lot. More and more, police stations everywhere may have to utilize TV surveillance cameras in guarding against such attacks. *(San Francisco Examiner photograph)*

Figure 24. Exterior surveillance camera at Park Station. *(DCPD photograph)*

JAIL COMPLEXES

Prisoner security is important and sometimes difficult to maintain. While the jailer is busy at one end of the jail, a prisoner at the other end may be busily engaged in hiding contraband, attempting escape, damaging the cells, or even committing suicide, assault, or murder. Cameras placed at strategic spots to monitor all of the activity within the jail provide insurance against all of these acts. We have found that television monitoring inhibits nearly all of the prisoners who go through the Daly City facility. The evidence of the television camera leads them to believe that they are constantly under someone's scrutiny, whether or not they are. A troublesome prisoner occasionally attempts to circumvent the system by wadding up wet toilet paper and throwing it at the cover glass on our ceiling-mounted cameras. He finds that this brings an immediate response from the officer charged with the jail, who is advised by the communications room of the act of the prisoner. Seldom have any second occurrences been noted. Scanning of the monitors by the communications center also frees officers who may be needed for other duties. A video tape recorder is also hooked into the monitors to enable the communications operators to tape an entire booking, from removal of the arrestee from the patrol car to his placement in a cell, with continual scanning thereafter as necessary. Television has increased the overall efficiency of the jail operation and has made the handling of prisoners far safer for the individual officers concerned.

SECURITY ASSISTANCE

In addition to providing internal and external security to the police station, television is becoming an increasingly important method of providing businesses, financial institutions, plants, and warehouses with their own protection at reduced costs. Every day, the business community finds a new use for television in its security arrangements. In our visually oriented society, it becomes more imperative to the executive to take advantage of the low cost factor and the high rate of return involved in an investment in television equipment.

To be of true service to these businesses, policemen should become acquainted with the new techniques available. They can be of meaningful assistance when called upon to consult with a firm to tighten up its particular weak spots.

Salesmen engaged in vending television equipment are anxious to demonstrate their wares for the police executive, not only with the idea of selling their product to the department, but for the advice that may lead to several commercial installations based on the adaptability of the product to a firm's unique problems.

Such a system is shown in Figure 5. There is a self-contained unit further described in Chapter X. When properly installed, this unit can prove a remarkable deterrent to the criminal bent upon robbery, burglary, or other crimes. Financial institutions, liquor stores, and other businesses that by their nature are likely to be attacked by gunmen, have shown a marked decrease in robberies as a result of similar installations. In fact, the federal government places emphasis on the necessity of doing this. Recent legislation makes it mandatory for federally insured financial operations to install comparable equipment.

A peripheral advantage of such installations can best be shown by the following incident that occurred in Daly City.

A take-out food store had a surveillance camera in operation for approximately one month when a suspect committed an assault with a deadly weapon upon a customer of the store. When the officers in the squad car arrived, the suspect had fled. No one on the premises could tell the investigating officer the name of the suspect but they did indicate that he was believed to be a resident of the immediate area. The manager of the store informed the officer of the video tape unit and offered to call the company and have the tape of the suspect's act removed from the unit. When the tape was replayed on a monitor, the officer recognized the suspect as one he had arrested on a previous occasion for another offense. Within one hour, the suspect was placed in custody for the felonious assault and when he was advised of the existence of the video tape, readily admitted his guilt. This admission also served to limit the court proceedings to a minimum.

VII

PROSECUTION

A s the finished police report summarizes all of the facts of a case
acquired through investigative techniques to achieve the goal of
successful prosecution, so the VTR program lends itself to the same
goal.

The chief uses VTR as a tool of communication and administration (Chapter II). Intelligence is gathered and disseminated by the
same means (Chapter III). The Detective Division resorts to VTR
as an investigative tool and notetaking device (Chapter IV).

Policemen are trained through this medium (Chapter V); building or bank security is upgraded by it (Chapter VI); and personnel are selected and trained as a team to properly utilize it (Chapters IX and XI). Proper equipment selection and knowledge of the capabilities and degree of sophistication of that equipment also enter into the picture (Chapters X and XI).

In the investigative sense, and in the belief that training and investigative efforts point to the goal of successful prosecution of the responsible malefactor, all of the other chapters of this book relate to this chapter. Here we deal with the sum total of all of our efforts, the successful prosecution of the criminal.

The problem of admissibility of evidence to court is always a specter. We have found no decision that indicates a blanket inadmissibility of VTR as evidence in a case. Our findings indicate that admissibility or inadmissibility of video tape as evidence depends precisely upon the statements in general. Sometimes they are admissible, and sometimes they are not.

We are prone to look upon VTR, in cases where it might be inadmissible, as "notes," to be reviewed by the investigating officer prior to his court appearance, in precisely the same manner as he would and should review his reports and notes prior to testifying.

Whether VTR is admitted or merely reviewed prior to testifying, its value becomes again apparent. Not only are words and pictures recorded in the notes, but so are extraneous sounds that tend to show the climate of a situation; voice intonations depict attitudes and facial expressions come forth as they never could in written notes.

As noted elsewhere in this writing, an entire crime scene can be transported to another location, in this instance to the jury box itself.

An officer makes an arrest. He admonishes the suspect of his rights. The suspect makes an admission or a confession. The matter goes to trial. The officer has a good case. What does the defense attorney attack? He is forced to attack the efficacy and truthfulness of the rights warning, the intelligent waiver of those rights by the suspect, and the statement itself.

The attorney, of necessity, will try to establish that the officer told the suspect of his rights by rote, that he did not truly communicate the fair import of the admonishment, and that, indeed, his client did not understand what he was doing or saying. The attorney may endeavor to establish that a coercive atmosphere existed at the time. He will try in every manner and way to attack the statement; the statement, he will seek to show, did not state what it is purported was stated and, if it did, the conclusion reached from it was erroneous in the extreme.

A video tape of the situation can negate this kind of argument. The voice intonations will show the attitude and whether the admonishment was understood or misunderstood. It will be apparent whether the waiver was an intelligent one; in fact, with the tape, the prosecutor will already have decided this. If he was in doubt, he would not be prosecuting.

The jury can decide from clear evidence what the suspect actually uttered, and, indeed, whether the atmosphere as depicted was coercive or not.

The only thing left for the defense attorney to do is to attack the admissibility of VTR as such. Even if he is successful in this ploy, the investigator has his "notes," which will transport him back to the scene for complete recollection prior to testifying.

In many areas, drunk driving suspects have been tested on film. These are often 16mm sound-on-film productions. While they were valuable, they suffer some severe drawbacks. One such drawback is the delay in processing of the film; again, VTR can accomplish the same goal while eliminating the expensive and time-consuming processing step. Indeed, it may even be possible to attack the chain of evidence with respect to the photograhpic processing step.

Many departments have suffered from the expense of the color sound-on-film tool. It is too expensive to employ the tool at length because of the number of drunk driving suspects processed. An administrative order read: "Hold filmed drunk driving tests to three minutes."

Problem: The tail wags the dog; the tool is not permitted to function to its full usefulness. Efficiency also suffers, for many drunks can steel themselves to act and function acceptably over the short haul. If the person is actually intoxicated to any degree, however, it is unlikely that he can steel himself sufficiently over a fifteen or twenty-minute period of VTR observation.

Should the suspect pass the test, the tape can be reused. Should he fail, the tape is retained for court evidence, and later is either reused or converted into training material.

In very recent times we have observed a disruption of the legal process vis-à-vis the courtroom. It is axiomatic that justice is a tenuous thing. It is also understood that the court adversary system will work only when the parties of both sides are predisposed to abide by the rules. The contestants in any "game" must play by at least general rules, or there cannot be a game.

This is why penalties are marched off on the football field and why boxers are called for fouling. Golfers can be penalized, even discredited and dismissed, for scorecard violations.

It is becoming more common for revolutionaries who are defendants in a court criminal matter to disrupt the proceedings as often as possible. Such procedures subvert and stain the proceedings; this causes either complete disruption of the matter at hand or summary action by the judge. Actions by the judge can then be appealed, discredited by loud cries of persecution, and headlined in the news media.

To some extent, the court system is fragile. To have to bind and restrain defendants in the courtroom, however justifiably, is repugnant to both the judge and the citizenry at large. It is also playing into the hands of the revolutionaries.

How can we solve the problem? Do we allow disruption to the point of chaos in the court? Do we use the ball-and-chain or strait-jacket approach? Both are ruinous.

Closed circuit or VTR television can be an answer. In the famous (or infamous) "Chicago Seven" trial, the constant violent demeanor on the part of the defendants caused major disruptions in the trial process. The judge ordered the defendants restrained, and later several of them and their attorneys received sentences for contempt of court.

Prosecutor Thomas Foran later stated that this action must be avoided in the future. It was, he said, the most horrifying thing he had ever witnessed in a courtroom. Mr. Foran suggested that in this type of situation in the future, the defendants should be placed in another room, and should observe the proceedings over television.

We agree. Disruptions could, in this fashion, be eliminated; at the same time, even though they would be physically removed from the courtroom, revolutionary defendants would not be tried in absentia. They would, in fact, be present, via television.

Penalizing of the participants occurs in any sporting event. Continued outbursts cause players' expulsion from the contest. While the judge did penalize in this contest, expulsion was more difficult. It may now be possible without compromising the proceedings.

VTR lends itself equally well to open tape recording and to surreptitious recording. We suggest that admissibility should be based on factors other than the mere use of the device; this is not unlike the usual problem affecting prosecution when microphones or "bugs" are used, where the tool and the processes are the matters under attack by the defense.

VTR can also help in identification of the suspect. Let us say that a suspect is captured and booked. The investigator arranges for a lineup of the suspect and others to be viewed by the victims. He takes all precautions to make it a fair lineup, protecting the suspect, and to make it a practical lineup, protecting the victimized persons.

He arranges to include individuals of the same race, size, and age as the suspect. He is careful to allow the suspect to choose his own place in the lineup. The defendant's attorney may be present.

The investigator must ascertain that nothing occurs to indicate the actual suspect to the victims. He will caution his victims not to speak during the process, and at no time to speak to each other before everyone has written his choice, if any, upon the card provided for this purpose.

We suggest that a video tape recording of the lineup would obviate the necessity for long arguments in court as to the efficacy and fairness of the lineup. The presence of VTR at the lineup may, in fact, insure that the investigator will be very careful, and will keep everyone present "honest."

Closed circuit jail surveillance television serves the same purpose, as discussed in Chapter VI. The VTR attachment to the closed circuit scanner can fix and lock in scenes of jail destruction and assaults on other prisoners. Many offenses are committed or attempted by jailed persons. These, like other crimes, are chargeable, and if they can be proved, the prisoners can be prosecuted. In such cases, VTR actually witnesses the crime being committed.

While examples of successful prosecution resulting from video tape recordings do not abound, this largely results from its newness, or at least its non-use. VTR can be utilized in court at any time when still photographs, motion pictures, or tape recorders would be admissible. VTR contains all of these techniques.

One successful prosecution stands out. In October 1968, there were anti-war demonstrations in San Francisco. Armed forces personnel were advised that they could participate as citizens, but they were warned that uniforms should not be worn or displayed while they demonstrated.

Air Force OSI investigators observed the large demonstration. They video taped pertinent portions for both intelligence and prosecutive purposes. Two cases were tried at courts-martial, based on video tape evidence.

An airman defied the order, wore his uniform, and made a public speech. In his speech, he read the order to the crowd. This was all video taped. The airman was court-martialed, and was convicted on the basis of this admissible evidence. The matter was appealed, and the conviction was upheld by the Court of Military Appeals. The airman is presently serving his sentence at Leavenworth.

Peripherally, the Air Force evidence was utilized to convict a Navy nurse at her court-martial for the same offense.

Thus, prosecutions have been aided by video tape evidence, and have been upheld on appeal.

VIII

BUYING NEW EQUIPMENT

BEFORE any police department invests in a new piece of equipment or hires a new man, a test or series of tests is generally undertaken. This insures that the man or the tool will fit into the the scheme of that department.

Salesmen are often quick to promise unusual abilities for their product and paint glowing word pictures of the seemingly magical powers their product has. The uninitiated might believe this, but hardly the experienced police administrator who has been "burned" before.

The ideas contained in this chapter are by no means novel or original. The discerning administrator will road test new automobiles for replacement of the police fleet. New weapons to be purchased are benchfired for accuracy and performance. The purchase of television equipment is sometimes made without any prior testing because of lack of experience in the field of electronics.

We found that salesmen approaching the Daly City Police Department with television equipment would happily give us all sorts of written handouts prepared by advertising agency personnel specifically for this end. When a test of the equipment was requested under conditions favorable to us and by personnel assigned to use the gear, many salesmen would never return. Good! They had enough sense, perhaps, to realize that the performance would not meet our requirements. With relative ease, we narrowed down the vendors to just two that were sincere in their approach and with whom we field tested many different pieces of television gear. Finally we arrived at our decision and presented our finding in writing to the chief of police for authorization to purchase the equipment.

The VTR personnel worked with us from the inception and were the ones who became the most discriminating in choosing the right item for each use (see Chapter IX).

We used the guidelines set down in preceding chapters for potential uses of the equipment. While keeping an eye on allocated funds, we were able to select a television package for the embryonic stage. We have since made several additions and modifications to the initial purchase. As the years progress, we plan future budgetary requirements to upgrade and implement our present equipment without deliberately making any of it obsolete. Our oldest pieces of gear are already several years old and still perform those tasks for which they were purchased. Since then, we have merely become more sophisticated and have added equipment to expand the efficiency of the original.

Service was included in the basic contract award and relieves us of having to provide specialized technical personnel to handle mechanical breakdowns. The vendor also is required to provide a suitable replacement item for one which is taken to the shop for maintenance or repair. This is a singularly important consideration for police who must be ready to serve seven days a week, twenty-four hours a day.

More and more departments are investing in video tape equipment. Some, in fact, are already capable of broadcasting. Many other departments are in the process of exploring the possibility of adding television as a tool in police work. For their guidance primarily, this chapter has outlined some preliminary thoughts to be considered beforehand.

The police administrator who is interested in the addition of television should first select the man to pilot the project. Whether he comes from the Training, Patrol, Special Services, or Detective divisions is decided largely by the primary function that video tape will serve in the department.

When the project leader has been briefed on his objectives and has done some preliminary reading and investigation of the general subject, he should spend some time in the selection of personnel (see Chapter IX).

Contact should then be made with the vendors to make arrangements to field test the equipment under a series of conditions that have been set up by the project leader.

After field testing and a general critique of the items needed compared with the items tested, a final run-through should be made of the package to be submitted as a recommendation to the chief of police.

IX

SELECTING THE TEAM

I N order to realize the most profit from the VTR program, the concerned department must invest the best possible equipment, training, and personnel into it. Here we will speak of the last factor, selection of the team personnel.

As with any specialized group of men, motivation and ability are paramount in the selection of team members. Members must have a proclivity for the work, and must be available to perform it.

A large department, having recognized and accepted the need for the program, will select team members on the same basis as the one it uses to appoint members to any necessary specialty. Small and medium-sized departments have a further problem, since VTR team duties will be corollary in nature: i.e., extra duties and not primary duties. If it is possible, then, such departments have to select and develop men who are even more motivated than are their opposite numbers who work full time on larger departments.

Team members must be intelligent and motivated persons. They need not necessarily be police officers. Team members can be selected from officers, records personnel, cadets, and the like. In addition to the qualities already mentioned, members should be male, and they must be in good physical condition. Because they will sometimes deal with matters that will be classified, they must be responsible and reliable with matters pertaining to vice and intelligence.

Any man working with VTR of necessity must be imaginative and innovative. At the same time each man has to be disciplined enough to be a student, a trainee, and a team member.

In the Daly City Police Department, we first consulted the skills files. From that repository we selected a number of potential candidates for the team. This was done by gleaning from the files men with the following attributes, qualifications, or attainments: language ability, high IQ, mechanical background, former successful affiliation with matters or callings based on teamwork and discipline, and a knowledge of graphics.

Having explained the program to the potential selectees, we accepted volunteers from that group. As always, there were more volunteers than needed, and as always, normal attrition winnowed the group down to an acceptable size.

Interest and dedication go together, and these qualities, coupled with training and experience, molded the VTR team into a functional and valuable group.

While this was a specialty group, no man specialized within the group. That is, each man rotated through and became experienced in each slot.

In the case of the small or medium-sized department, where it is necessary to assign VTR to volunteers as a corollary duty, it is essential to have the selection spread over all watches. Thus, if emergent conditions dictate the fielding of a VTR group on little notice, there will always be someone qualified on duty.

The formal makeup of the team is relatively simple. A basic team must have a cameraman. If he is operating a battery pack, then it is possible, though not desirable, to function with the one man. The suggested basic team consists of a cameraman and a tape deck operator. If possible, and hopefully, a unit leader should also be present.

The medium-sized department team should consist of a unit leader, a director, two camera operators, a deck and mixer operator, and an audio technician. We hope and recommend that the team members will each be cross-trained in the other's job. In this case, the unit leader need not necessarily be connected exclusively with the VTR team. While the director, camera operators, deck man, and audio technician need to be assigned to those duties for the duration of the detail, the unit leader might also be the patrol or detective leader. This, in fact, might be recommended out of consideration for coordinating the entire effort—that of the operation and that of the supporting VTR group. It may prevent a collision of empires.

These procedures are equally effective when the team is posted to the Training Division for staged training or field training, or when the team is detailed to an actual field problem or assignment.

X

THE EQUIPMENT

DESCRIBED and depicted in this chapter are some of the basic needs of the police television function. All that is really necessary to make television a reality for a department is to obtain the items that are illustrated in the Frontispiece to Chapter I. We should make two points clear at the outset. We are not selling any equipment nor does the appearance of any brand in this book represent an endorsement. Space limitations make it impossible for us to either describe or portray the full range of closed circuit television equipment that is on the market. Because a company is not mentioned in this book does not mean that we are not aware of its products. As we have stressed earlier, the purchase of equipment will depend upon its availability in a given geographical area and what particular needs it will serve (see Chapter VIII).

We feel that police television is not expected to be of "network" quality. Closed circuit equipment is depicted and described because of space limitations and because there are very few departments that can afford to become "broadcast-capable." To those few departments, this chapter will not be necessary. Broadcast equipment is highly expensive and requires professional engineering to become a reality. But for the greater number of departments, closed circuit equipment is the type that is available. In order to make these writings more meaningful, we have attempted to arrange the equipment by price range, from the least expensive to the higher-priced and more sophisticated.

There are at present two sizes of tape used in closed circuit TV: one inch and one-half inch. One-inch equipment is larger, bulkier, and more costly than the smaller and more compact half-inch gear. We have not included any information about television receivers or monitor since they vary little in size and price. However, we suggest that at least two of them be purchased. One should be of the small nine-inch-screen size for use in concert with the tape desk while recording and for playback to small limited audiences, generally of not more than three persons. A larger nineteen to twenty-three-inch monitor will accommodate groups up to twenty adequately. For extremely large groups Tele-Beam projectors are available that will project the television picture onto regular motion picture screens some eight to ten feet in size.

For small departments with limited budgets, the most useful piece of equipment will be the battery pack camera. Figure 25 shows one in the back-carrying position and Figure 26 shows one in the shoulder-

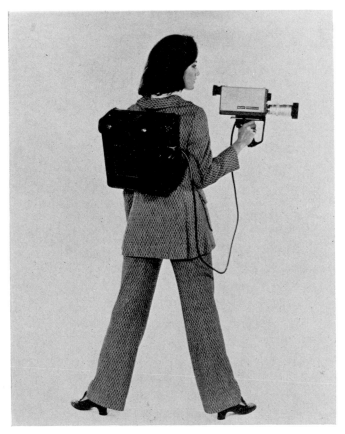

Figure 25. Portable camera in backpack position. (*Sony Corporation*)

carrying position. Figure 27 indicates how the camera can be placed for playback and instant previewing, using the eyepiece, while still in the field. The manufacturer's suggested price is slightly under $1,500.

For use with the battery pack camera and others is the half-inch tape deck depicted in Figure 28. This deck is very light and easily transported, as seen in Figure 29. The cost is about $700.

For studio and cabled use to the tape deck mentioned above, Sony has a compact ensemble that fits into a light but rugged carrying

Figure 26. Shibaden battery pack camera. *(DCPD photograph)*

Figure 27. Sony battery pack camera and Porta-Deck. *(Sony Corporation)*

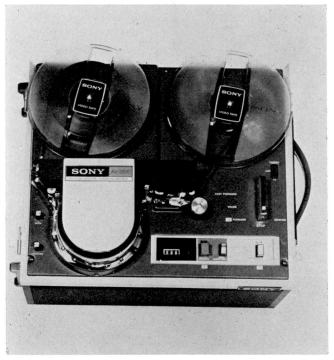

Figure 28. Sony AV-3600 portable deck. *(Sony Corporation)*

Figure 29. The tape deck weighs 33 pounds, and is easy to carry. *(Sony Corporation)*

case and includes all the equipment shown in Figure 30. It sells for about $700. This particular camera also comes without the viewfinder (the upper portion of the camera divided by the black line). Without the viewfinder the ensemble sells for approximately $400. A viewfinder is, in essence, a small two-inch-square television monitor. It is strongly suggested that regardless of the type of camera that is purchased, it should have a viewfinder. This makes production work easier and lessens the margin for error.

Figure 31 shows a studio-type camera which has a viewfinder and which is mounted with a zoom lens. This studio camera is heavier and has a slightly larger viewfinder, and is of the type that lends

Figure 30. Sony 2300 studio-type camera. All of the gear pictured fits into the carrying case. *(Sony Corporation)*

itself well to indoor camera work. Almost all of the lower-priced cameras have C-ring mountings for the lens and any 16mm lens can be screwed in for long-distance work on surveillances. This camera averages $1,000 in price. It is used in connection with a one-inch tape deck as shown in Figure 32. This video tape recorder costs $2,350. A larger and heavier-duty one-inch tape deck is shown in Figure 33.

A specialized video tape deck recently introduced and ideal for security surveillances is the one pictured in Figure 9. The time lapse recorder uses one-inch tape and can be adjusted to take pictures for up to sixty hours of surveillance on a single one-hour reel at the rate

Figure 31. A compact viewfinder television camera for closed circuit production work. Camera resolution is 600 lines at center and 400 lines at corners. The model CC-450 camera has a full-bandwidth signal-to-noise ratio of 40 dB (*Ampex Corporation*)

of one frame per hour. It can also be adapted to a Polaroid R camera for still photographs depicting any significant frame. This tape deck costs about $4,500.

When a department wishes to become more sophisticated and wants to be able to produce various special effects and use a two-camera chain, while still having the advantages of a portable unit, something along the lines of the "studio in a package" illustrated in operation in Figure 34 might be the answer. The entire studio fits in three carrying cases and can be handled by two men. The basic package includes the control panel and three monitors, two studio cameras, and all the accessory equipment necessary to operate them upon unpacking. The entire basic package costs approximately $10,000 and can be expanded with an additional camera and two additional monitors.

Figure 32. The Ampex VR 5100E is one of the lowest-priced 1-inch video tape recorders capable of high-quality assemble editing of any monochrome video signal. The new closed circuit video tape recorder features assemble editing and independent record capability. *(Ampex Corporation)*

From this point, additional equipment can be added to all of the basic purchases and further new equipment considered. Some of the new innovations in specialized cameras that will appear on the market in the years to come are almost science fiction in their concepts, but true. At the time of this writing, Singer-General Precision Laboratories is beginning to market a low-light-level camera that virtually takes pictures in the dark even at extreme distances and that will be ideal for use in surveillance and security operations at night when no light source is available.

Smaller security-type cameras are available that are no larger than five inches by seven inches and that weigh less than three pounds. They are easy to install and conceal and have hundreds of commercial applications.

Figure 33. An Ampex VR 7500 closed circuit video tape recorder is used at a ski school. Ski lessons are recorded and viewed immediately by student and instructor. The simple closed circuit television system consists of a recorder, television camera, TV receiver, and tape. (*Ampex Corporation*)

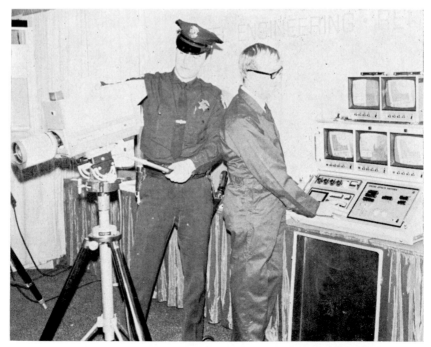

Figure 34. Telenetics "studio in a package." (*DCPD photograph*)

When a department becomes sophisticated to the point of requiring a formal studio, as the Daly City Police Department did, consulting engineers will be required to draft formal plans for facilities. A projected studio for our department, showing the studio itself and the master control room, is portrayed in Figure 35.

Figure 35. Projected studio (*A*) and master control room, (*B*), Daly City Police Department. (*Don Campbell*)

XI

TRAINING THE TEAM

SINCE we have already decided upon the personnel and equipment, the next obvious step is to instruct the personnel in the mechanics of television production as it will relate to the police function. Having selected men who have a knowledge of graphics makes this task that much easier. They should have already been exposed to the equipment and have no "fear" of it.

What remains is to lay out the guidelines of the production group. How will it relate to the particular use to be made of the team and the equipment within a department's framework?

We have stressed the necessity of "cross-training" the team members who may upon occasion be required to perform any or all of the necessary duties within the scope of the team performance. Dispersing the members to different watches makes available to the department, at any hour, someone competent to handle the equipment. This may be one man or several.

Liaison between the various levels of production of the program. The Training Division, for example, is and should be responsible for deciding the subject matter to be filmed. The instructor will be designated by the same division. A conference should then be arranged with the director, instructor, and a member of the training staff responsible for the material to be presented.

Conferences such as this will define the mission of the training session. The Training Division has already decided what will be taught. The instructor has his own ideas on how it will be taught. The director will be held responsible for how it will be filmed. Suggestions can be made by the director as to the locale and scenery necessary to enhance the visual picture. If training aids are to be used, are they of the proper size and color for good reproduction?

When the conference has mutually decided on the time, place, and equipment to be used, the director will return to his unit and prepare for the session. Some blocking out should be done so that camera placement and lighting are considered and prepared. Audio placement can be provided based on the filming to be done. Any necessary props and training aids will be collected. Finally, the director will assign his team members to their roles for that session. The director functions as the coordinator of the activity. His job will not be to change material or methods but to make the material or methods as visually acceptable as possible.

THE CAMERA OPERATOR

The heart of the the team is the camera and its operator. He will sometimes be the only member of the team and therefore he must be able to consider all the applications of the video tape operation. The camera operation, taken by itself, can be thought of as having three main roles:

1. Picture composition.
2. Focus or depth of field.
3. Lighting or monochromatic color.

Picture Composition

When we use the camera in television production, the cameraman is generally the one responsible for the camera shots and the framing of those shots. In larger teams, the director will assign the shots to the camera, so the operator should have some idea of the production terms used (see Figs. 36-41). To best describe the types of shots to be taken, we will show how each shot would look framed in the viewfinder.

Very Long Shot

Pictures simplify explanations. Therefore, in shooting exterior tapes, it is sometimes effective to use the very long shot to establish the locale with a minimum of explanation (Fig. 42). To be used effectively, the very long shot should be used sparingly to create an overall impression of the environment; it is most effective in opening sequ-

Figure 36. "Stand by. Go ahead!" *(Don Campbell)*

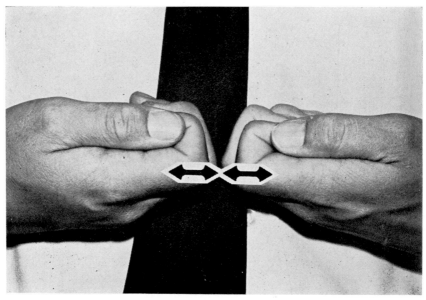

Figure 37. "Slow down. Stretch it out." *(DCPD photograph)*

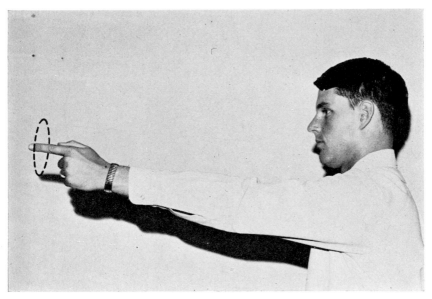

Figure 38. "Wind up now." *(DCPD photograph)*

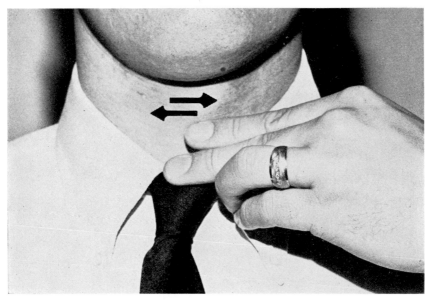

Figure 39. "Cut it. Omit rest of item." *(DCPD photograph)*

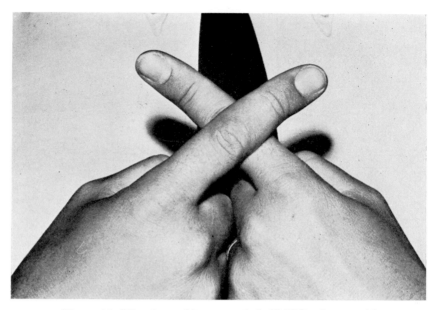

Figure 40. "You have thirty seconds." *(DCPD photograph)*

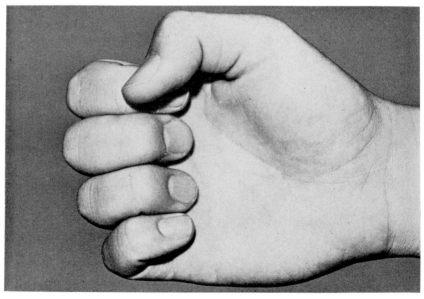

Figure 41. "You have fifteen seconds." *(DCPD photograph)*

Figure 42. Very long shot. *(DCPD photograph)*

ences that establish or set the stage for the scenes to follow. Periodically, the same type of shot can be used to "fade out" of an outdoor sequence.

Long Shot

Moving the camera from the very long shot, which creates the illusion necessary, to the long shot helps establish more details, and brings the focus of the viewer's attention onto the type of action that will be taking place (Fig. 43). As an example, a riot is being taped, and the very long shot has established the setting in overall terms; moving the camera into the long shot establishes what is to be

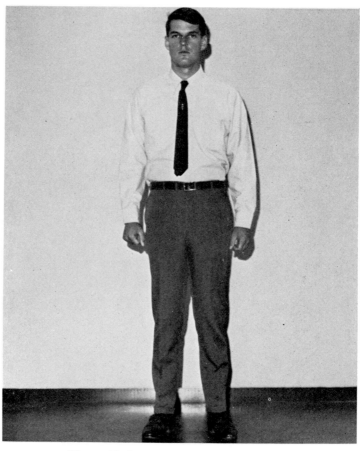

Figure 43. Long shot. *(DCPD photograph)*

filmed in specific terms. From the confusion of the scene, the viewer is forced by the camera to focus his attention on the individual or individuals in conflict.

Full-Length Framing

The last of the overall shots to be considered is the type of picture that brings the individual into full focus. It is the most effective type of shot to use if overall body action or movements are to be considered. In demonstrating a police practice—the use of weapons, for example—it is necessary that the viewer see the entire body and its movements to appreciate the importance of such things as body stance and its correlation to the removal of the weapon from its holster.

Three-Quarter-Length and Middle Shots

These two types of shots are generally similar in nature and their effective use depends on the cameraman. When working in areas where body movement is important to the film, it is necessary to select a shot which will not lose any of the movement by letting it go abruptly out of camera range. A middle shot would not be the best if we wished to portray the drawing of a weapon from the holster, since the action would be taking place below the range of the lens and would require jerky movements of the camera to capture the proper picture (Figs. 44-46).

Closeup Shots

These shots direct the viewer's interest to a particular point of emphasis (Figs. 47-50). From a psychological standpoint, these are the most poignant and, as the word implies, the most acute. If a camera is used effectively in closeups, the entire message can be made clear with a minimum of narration. But most operators have a tendency to overdo the closeup and to minimize the very effect for which they are striving. Their attitude should be: "Get the shot and get out!" With overemphasis, closeups lose their effectiveness and make the average viewer uncomfortable. From a technical standpoint, closeups also present a problem in focus and, if they are held too long, the action becomes hard for the cameraman to follow.

Figure 44. Three-quarter shot. (*DCPD photograph*)

Figure 45. Mid-shot. *(DCPD photograph)*

Figure 46. Waist shot. *(DCPD photograph)*

Figure 47. Chest shot. *(DCPD photograph)*

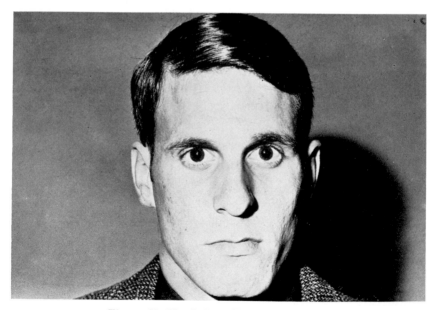

Figure 48. Head shot. *(DCPD photograph)*

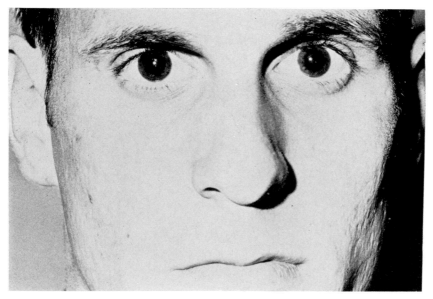

Figure 49. Full-face shot. *(DCPD photograph)*

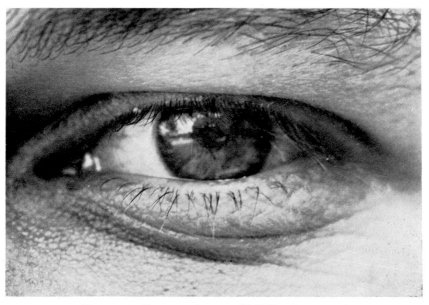

Figure 50. Extreme closeup. *(DCPD photograph)*

For the most effective use of the camera and a minimum of focusing problems, it appears that a zoom-type lens is the best for the small department. It is strongly suggested that all cameras be equipped with variable zoom lenses for maximum use and minimum problems. With rare exceptions, the zoom lens covers the broad range of shots that we have just described.

After practicing the various types of shots available with the camera, attention should be given to the proper framing of the picture within the viewfinder and on the television monitor (Figs. 51-54). Nothing is more disconcerting to the viewer than to be treated to the sight of an unbalanced picture. This is one of the areas that requires the knowledge and the use of graphics. Simply stated, if we are to show the viewer a picture of the chief of police in his office and we wish to properly frame the picture, we should have an equal amount of open space on both sides and at the top. This allows the person being filmed some freedom of movement and will actually require less work by the cameraman. Figures 47, 51, and 53 are good examples of the proper use of framing.

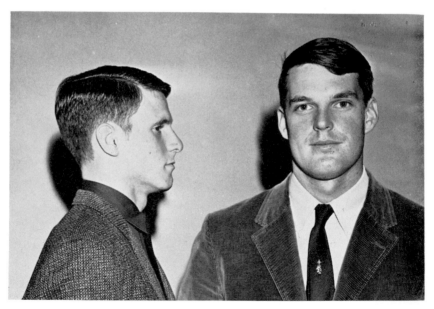

Figure 51. When framing a shot using more than one person, balance such as is illustrated is generally suggested. *(DCPD photograph)*

Figure 52. Full-face closeups are rarely as effective as in Figure 51. *(DCPD photograph)*

Figure 53. When trying to frame more than two persons, it may be necessary to triangulate the subjects for the best balance. *(DCPD photograph)*

Figure 54. This is an example of poor framing. *(DCPD photograph)*

If the cameraman is to function as the sole member of the team, he should have some idea of the action that will take place and adjust his movements accordingly. If the event to be filmed is to be staged, such as a training session, the cameraman should block out the action to take place and plan to work his shots to the best advantage. Blocking is merely walking through the sequence beforehand and selecting the best location for the camera in advance. Returning to our example of the portrayal of shooting the pistol, what can we learn from the session if the cameraman is taking his shots from the left side of a right-handed shooter?

Focus or Depth of Field

Since most policemen have used some form of camera, they should be familiar with the value of a sharply focused picture and the proper use of depth of field. There is little difference in this regard between the television camera and the still camera. Simply defined, depth of field is the distance from the nearest to the farthest points that are in focus with a particular focal length, distance, and aperture opening. If we were to imagine that the area to be photographed were divided into thirds and that the first third was immediately in front of the camera, the middle third was farther out, and the final third was farthest out, the most sharply focused area would be the middle third.

Depth of field is affected by the relationship of three factors: the distance from camera to subject, the focal length, and the aperture or iris setting. As we have mentioned earlier, the most practical type of lens to use is the zoom lens, which permits instants adjustment to the focal length of the lens. Most available zoom lenses cover a span from approximately ten to ninety millimeters. This measurement is known as the focal length. For most very long and long shots, smaller focal lengths are needed; these are usually wide-angle shots. A good rule of thumb is that the fewer the millimeters, the longer the shot. With practice one also arrives at the best focal length setting for the type of shot desired.

When focal length and camera-to-subject distances are held constant, a smaller aperture or *f*-stop will increase the depth of field. The iris is set according to the amount of light reflected from the area to be taped. If there is strong light intensity, the aperture is made smaller. As the light decreases, the *f*-stop becomes larger. It is possible, therefore, to increase the depth of field simply by increasing the lighting reflected from the scene. Lighting is the most practical method but not the only method of increasing depth of field. We can also achieve the same effect by adding more distance to the area between the camera and the subject.

Experimentation with these three factors will add to the cameraman's knowledge and he will be able to establish his own tables to follow in future enterprises.

Lighting or Monochromatic Color

The use of lighting will be covered in detail in the section on the lighting operator; we will discuss here differences in tonal gradations using the black and white camera, as well as camera detail and quality. Lighting obviously increases the detail and quality of the picture, but there are other factors in television camera work to be considered. Picture detail in this sense generally refers to the number of horizontal lines of resolution that are available. The average video tape system should be able to reproduce approximately three hundred lines of resolution. Detail is being able to distinguish between adjacent areas of differing tones. Tonal gradations are important in establishing a sharp, crisp picture. In black and white equipment, the number of tonal gradations is extremely limited. Tones run in intensity from very brilliant white through progressive tones of gray to total black. Extremes should be avoided. A brilliant white generally reflects too much light and blossoms on all the objects near it, causing a decided lack of definition. Numerical ratings from 1 through 10 should be mentally assigned to the various shades, beginning with brilliant white as number 1 and total black as number 10. For the best definition and contrast, only the shades from 3 through 7 should be used. We must also consider that for the best effect, a background should be used that is several tones darker than the subject to be filmed. If the officers wear a khaki uniform, they should be placed in front of a brown background. If they are garbed in light blue uniforms, a dark blue backdrop would be most effective. And for the many departments that wear dark blue uniforms, a gray or light blue backdrop might be the most effective. When visual aids are to be used, the most effective arrangement is white lettering on a black background. But because white and black are so opposite in contrast, no more than three lines should be used on any visual aid; with more, the picture tube tends to drop off in definition at the edges and the effect is lost.

THE TAPE DECK OPERATOR

When a cabled camera is employed, there is a need for an operator who remains at the tape deck controls to set the controls, establish the audio levels, and start and stop the deck while the cameraman is working. A typical tape deck is shown in Figure 55. From the deck, the operator can also view a small monitor and direct the activities of the cameraman and others engaged in the filming.

THE LIGHTING OPERATOR

It is not a necessity in smaller crews to assign a crew member specifically as a lighting operator; these duties can be handled by other members of the crew and are usually done in advance of the

Figure 55. Ampex VR 5100 tape recorder: (1) Audio level meter. (2) Audio record level control. (3) Tension control. (4) Video level meter. (5) Video record level control. (6) Tracking. (7) Record interlock button. (8) Record button. (9) Play button. (10) Stop button. (11) Rewind-fast forward control. (12) Record-play lever. (13) Ready-thread. (14) Power on indicator. (15) Digital counter. (16) On-volume control. *(Ampex Corporation)*

taping. In larger operations, where several areas or sets are to be employed, it may be necessary to assign a man to handle the changing of the lights.

As mentioned earlier in this chapter, the lighting of the scene is important to achieving the best picture. Basically, there are three types of lighting that are important to the well-made video tape.

Base Light

This type of lighting is also referred to as *soft lighting* and is used to uniformly cover the entire area to be filmed with shadowless light. This light is generally placed in a position near the camera, its exact location depending on the set to be lit. It should be placed in such a way as to keep all camera and microphone boom movements as free from shadows as possible.

Back Lighting

A back light is just that, one that is placed behind, above, and slightly off-center from the subject to be taped. This type of lighting can also be called *halo lighting*. It is used to add dimension to the subject and to help him stand out in marked contrast to the background, creating the illusion of depth. Removing the back light will give a flat one-dimensional impression to the picture.

Key Lighting

Often called the "actor's friend," key lighting chisels the features of the performer and makes them take on the extra dimension necessary to add character to the picture. Where the base light removes shadows, the key light accentuates those facial shadows that properly belong in the well-lit picture.

These three types of lighting are the ones most commonly used in both film and television productions; with practice, the proper placement takes little time. Further experimentation will produce many other artistic effects.

When lighting is to be done away from a studio, in the daylight, for example, sunlight is the best type of lighting. However, there are times when even Mother Nature must be given a helping hand. If the out-of-doors setting is in an area where the sunlight has no direct effect on the scene, it may be necessary to assist with mirrored boards to balance the light and remove dark shadows from the faces of the subjects. These mirrors can be effective if they are properly placed, and can balance the lighting with little cost. Any shiny, reflective surface can be utilized for this end. We have found that one of the most inexpensive of these is aluminum foil tacked onto hard composition backgrounds.

At night or on dull days, a motion picture "sun-gun" can be added to the tripod holding the camera to increase the lighting.

THE AUDIO OPERATOR

Television is a medium that not only records action and movement but also captures sound. The proper use and placement of microphones is important to achieve the maximum effect for the overall production. It is important for the audio technician to understand and appreciate the proper usage of the audio equipment that is available to him. Most video tape decks are equipped with a VU (volume in units or decibels of sound) or audio level meter (see Figure 55). For the best results the VU needle should register in the range between seventy to ninety decibels. This allows the louder noises to "peak" at the area of ninety to one hundred decibels and the lower noises to be captured at lower decibel levels. When a single microphone is used, it is important to keep the sound adjusted at the proper levels to maintain optimum performance. Audio control may be exercised by the tape deck operator or, in larger operations, it may be necessary to assign a special audio man to handle this task. Working with a minimum of equipment and having no sound mixing equipment may make it necessary to have several microphones planted around the area of the action and several hookups and disconnections from the sound source input, which is generally located on the rear of the video tape deck. This is not usually suggested, since there is a good chance of making the wrong connection or of obtaining varying levels of audio quality.

Some video tape decks are equipped with automatic gain controls that act as an automatic sound leveler. In certain instances, this can be a disadvantage, if voice sound is recorded at the same level as extraneous background noises. In one instance, we were recording an outside sequence when the sound of a train whistle some three blocks away came in with the same consistency of sound as the voice of the narrator.

The audio operator should be familiar with the various types of microphones that are available and the best use for each one. Basically there are four types:

1. The *cardioid microphone* has a semicircular pickup pattern; that is, it can detect those sounds originating in a 180-degree arc in front of the microphone. This eliminates any extraneous sounds that may be coming from the opposite side of the microphone face. This is the kind most generally in use in studios and is usually found hanging from a boom.

2. The *unidirectional microphone* serves the same purpose except that the pickup pattern is not as wide in the degree of

peripheral sounds that can be recorded. It eliminates some fifteen degrees of area on either side. If a shotgun type of microphone were needed, this would fill the bill.

3. *Bidirectional microphones* are the type that is usually used in recording panel discussions. This microphone will pick up sound from the front and rear but eliminates noise from the sides.

4. *Nondirectional microphones* can record sounds from a 360-degree radius and are most difficult to use in most cases because of the lack of control. If they are used in most studio or set locations, they tend to pick up all noises; this requires the utmost of control at the recording point.

Most of the microphones available on the market today have switches which can be used to change the setting from a unidirectional to a nondirectional function. In this respect, one microphone can be used for two separate functions.

Microphone placement, therefore, is determined not only by what is to be recorded but by the type of microphone that is used. It is generally agreed upon by professionals that microphones should be "heard and not seen." The diminutive size of the microphones available make them easy to conceal on a set. If they are to be used on a desk or table, some simple prop, such as a book, can be used to anchor and conceal them from sight. If there is to be only one speaker, he can be equipped with a lavaliere or lipstick type of microphone that will fit around his neck and can be concealed by a coat or even a tie. When fitting one of these microphones on a subject, the audio operator should insure that it is securely fastened to the material, to guard against any rustling that may result from body movements during the recording (Fig. 56).

For most police productions, it is not necessary to use a boom microphone, since they generally require another man to operate an additional piece of equipment and also require more care in following the movements of the performer. If a boom microphone is to be used, the boom operator must make sure that it is not obvious in the picture or causing a shadow on the picture. He must be able to anticipate any sudden movements of the subject, which is rather difficult to do, even by the best of professionals.

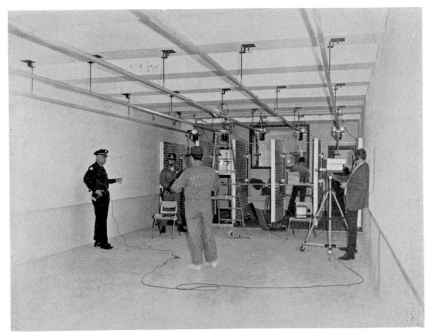

Figure 56. The indoor range does double duty as a studio. The crew and the performers discuss the situation between "takes." *(DCPD photograph)*

Finally, the audio operator should, where possible, use earphones to keep track of the sound that is being recorded. Without them, he is distracted from his primary function, which is control of the audio portion of the recording. Earphones, at first, can appear bothersome, but they can make an important contribution to the effective control of the sounds that are bing placed on the final product. Since there will be a great deal of activity going on around the audio operator, it is sometimes impossible for him to detect audio flaws over the background noise, and sound corrections will tend to be hit or miss.

TRAINING WITH OTHER SPECIALIZED UNITS

Whenever another special detail takes to the field for training, a valuable opportunity exists to further the training of the VTR team.

If, as we have mentioned in Chapter V, the anti-sniper team is detailed to the range for training, it behooves the department to send the VTR team along, which will serve two purposes. The special unit will be filmed performing its assigned role and will have a tape to use as a critique at the end of that session. The VTR team will not only be filming the activity but in essence furthering its own training in the process. The same tape that will be used as a critique for the special unit then becomes a critique for the members of the VTR team. Were good shots present or missing? Were camera operators in the right spot when the action was in progress? Were any unusual situations noted and can they be used to better advantage?

Aside from the Training role, the special unit will be called upon to perform its assignment. As a practical matter, in most cases it will be important to have a taped record of the unit's actions. Since both units have worked together in training sessions, they will both have become used to the other's method of operating and should function smoothly under fire.

This is the proof of the pudding or of the joining together of several parts to become a whole. In this case several special details have become part of a larger and more efficient task force.

INDEX